GLOBAL STANDARD
FOR FOOD SAFETY

INTERPRETATION GUIDELINE

June 2012

British Retail Consortium

London: TSO

information & publishing solutions

Published by TSO (The Stationery Office) and available from:

Online
www.brcbookshop.com

Mail, Telephone, Fax & E-mail
TSO
PO Box 29, Norwich NR3 1GN
Telephone orders/General enquiries: 0870 600 5522
Fax orders: 0870 600 5533
E-mail: book.orders@tso.co.uk
Textphone 0870 240 3701

TSO@Blackwell and other Accredited Agents

Liability

Copyright

For more information about BRC, contact

British Retail Consortium
Second Floor
21 Dartmouth Street
London
SW1H 9BP
Tel: +44 (0) 20 7854 8900
Fax: +44 (0) 20 7854 8901
email: brcglobalstandards@brc.org.uk
website: www.brcglobalstandards.com

Printed in the United Kingdom for The Stationery Office
J002628764   C7.5   07/12

Contents

Appendices   **107**

Sources of Further Information   **119**

SECTION I

EXPLAINING CERTIFICATION

Section I

Explaining Certification

1   Introduction

This Guideline is designed to give guidance on how to obtain certification to Issue 6 of the *Global Standard for Food Safety* (the Standard) and the implementation of individual requirements across all food industry sectors. Examples are given to explain the type of documents, procedures and level of detail that would be required by a certification auditor.

The contents of the Guideline are designed to help interpret the Standard; however, the exact requirements for any particular product, process or site will be specific to that industry and situation. Users of the Guideline are therefore cautioned not to rely solely on the information provided here, but also to reconfirm needs on a product-by-product basis. Both legislative and voluntary safety requirements change frequently, highlighting the need for regular checks of precise requirements.

Whilst adherence to the Guideline does not specifically form part of the requirement to achieve certification to the Standard, companies will need to demonstrate that they have taken account of the topics addressed within this Guideline. Examples are given as points to consider but should always be used in the correct context relevant to the business. Practices should be able to withstand challenge by an auditor and be in line with good industry practices.

Achieving a particular requirement is based on evidence collected and observations made during the audit, and on the procedures expected within that industry sector. The level of non-conformity assigned by an auditor against a requirement of the Standard is an objective judgement with respect to severity and risk, and is based on the evidence seen during the audit and independently verified by the Certification Body management.

2   BRC Certification

2.1   Why is BRC certification required?

Certification to the BRC Global Standard was developed to establish a common standard for food hygiene, allowing brand owners to demonstrate control and satisfy legal responsibility for products and consumer safety, as well as reducing audit duplication for manufacturers. The *Global Standard for Food Safety* has become a benchmark for best practice and is recognised worldwide by brand owners and manufacturers in the supply chain, with more than 15,000 food companies now certificated to the Standard. Certification is required when a customer requests, or a company wants to confirm by independent third-party audit, that operations meet a stated standard.

The *Global Standard for Food Safety* has been developed for manufacturers of food; however, certification throughout the supply chain is available through:

- *Global Standard for Packaging and Packaging Materials*
- *Global Standard for Consumer Products*
- *Global Standard for Storage and Distribution.*

2.2   What's new for Issue 6 of the Standard?

Following widespread consultation with international stakeholders representing food manufacturers, retailers, food service companies and Certification Bodies, Issue 6 of the Standard was developed to have a greater focus on:

- Improving consistency within the audit process.

- Ensuring that new developments in food safety have been effectively addressed.

- Providing greater choice in audit options – the unannounced audit programme remains voluntary but has been expanded to provide two options, designed to provide solutions to the concerns previously raised regarding the practical application of an unannounced audit. Sites can now choose an announced audit, a fully unannounced audit or a two-part audit consisting of an unannounced factory-based audit predominantly looking at good manufacturing practices (GMPs), followed by a planned (announced) second audit predominantly reviewing documentation and records.

- Encouraging adoption of the enrolment programme as a means of improving food safety in facilities where processes are in development. The scheme is specifically designed to recognise improvements in food safety by providing a scored audit (along with the full audit report) which can be shared with customers and used to focus further development activity.

3 First Steps to Gaining Certification

3.1 Self-audit or gap analysis

Once the decision has been made by the company to pursue certification to the Standard, the requirements need to be understood. The site needs to be assessed with regard to its current status, and areas that need to be improved must be identified. This may, for example, relate to the structure of buildings, equipment requirements, the design of processes or the documentation and implementation of procedures. The company needs to establish an action plan.

A copy of the Standard needs to be obtained and is a requirement of clause 1.1.7. Relevant staff need to understand what is expected. Training courses or further information are available and may be useful. Companies that are new to certification standards are recommended to join the enrolment programme at the earliest opportunity, as registration provides access to the BRC website (www.brcglobalstandards.com). A range of tools for developing companies will be made available on this website.

A gap analysis or self-audit needs to be conducted. This could be undertaken in-house – for example, incorporated into the company's internal audit process. However, it may require external resources in the form of consultancy expertise, or a pre-assessment may be undertaken by the company's chosen Certification Body.

Once the company has reviewed the gaps between the requirements and its current practices, the company's senior management needs to establish a plan to ensure that work is undertaken to fulfil the requirements. This could include, for example, updating of policies and procedures, training of staff, capital expenditure for equipment and maintenance of the building.

3.2 Who undertakes certification audits?

The BRC does not undertake the audits itself. The BRC is the Standard owner, documenting the requirements on behalf of stakeholders and controlling the operation of the certification scheme. The Standard is written by a committee of international representatives, coordinated by the BRC, including retailers, food industry representatives and Certification Bodies. The Global Standards team then controls how audits are undertaken through the specification of the audit protocol and supporting rules and regulations for companies undertaking certification audits (known as Certification Bodies). Monitoring of Certification Bodies is undertaken through independent accreditation – for example, by the United Kingdom Accreditation Service (UKAS) or the American National Standards Institute (ANSI), operating to internationally recognised protocols – and by the BRC Global Standards team.

Therefore, a BRC-approved Certification Body needs to be selected by the company. There is a worldwide choice of such bodies; a list can be found at www.brcdirectory.com. Certification Bodies need to be appropriately qualified to undertake the audit and conform to the company's and its customers' requirements.

3.3   Cost of audits

Audit costs vary and are set by the individual Certification Bodies. They may include the expenses of the auditor (for example, travel). Typically, the audit consists of two days on site, depending on factors such as company size (in terms of staff numbers and size of site), the complexity of the manufacturing process, communication difficulties (e.g. language) and difficulties during the audit. (A full list of factors is given in the Standard, Section III, paragraph 7.3.) In addition, time is needed to write up the report – typically 0.5–1 day. As with most purchases, the cost should be clearly stated and agreed between the company and the Certification Body prior to entering into the contract.

It should be noted that certification is a continual process, and it is a feature of the scheme that the Certification Body has the option to visit a certificated company at any stage of certification to ensure that certification principles are being upheld. This may arise through the receipt of further information, such as a complaint from a customer of the site, and a charge may be made for any subsequent visits or investigations.

An administration fee is payable directly to the BRC through the Certification Body for every audit undertaken; currently this is £125.

The company also needs to consider costs that may be incurred to ensure the company is operating to the standards required by the Global Standard, including site standards, as well as training and procedural costs.

3.4   When can the audit be undertaken?

The company and the chosen Certification Body should agree a mutually convenient date for audits and re-audits to ensure that the company retains ongoing certification. (For certificated sites this may be yearly or six-monthly, depending on the grade attained, and for sites in the enrolment programme the audit frequency is also yearly.) The company may wish to choose a date when:

- products that need to be included within the scope of the certificate are being manufactured
- personnel to be involved in the audit process are available.

Ongoing re-audit dates need to be considered since the re-audit date will fall between 11 and 12 months from the original audit date (or 5–6 months from the original audit date if a grade C is obtained, where re-audit is required after 6 months). Ensure the time of year is suitable for your company in years to come.

4   What to Expect on the Audit Day(s)

The auditor/Certification Body shall have confirmed to the company the time of arrival on site and may have provided an outline of the plan of the audit schedule. The duration of the audit, although planned in advance, will depend on the activities on the day, but it may be shortened by a well-organised site and information provided in advance as requested by the Certification Body.

The auditor will start with an opening meeting, which all the relevant company personnel (including the most senior production or operations manager on site) need to attend, to outline how the audit will be undertaken. This will enable agreement and organisation in terms of:

- staff who need to be available to discuss specific aspects
- documents that need to be provided
- rooms that need to be provided (e.g. consider where records are stored and how they can be supplied to the auditor)
- logistics to ensure that equipment, such as protective clothing, is provided.

The auditor is likely to require background details on the company and the process before any site tour, and may therefore look through a number of documents, including:

- company quality policies
- organisation structure

■   Hazard Analysis Critical Control Point (HACCP) documents.

Often, auditors will ask the company to carry out a traceability test whilst the auditor is on site, so it may be beneficial to start this process as soon as practical to allow collation of documents.

The auditor will need to see the manufacturing process in operation around the site, checking and challenging the operation of the company's procedures. The auditor will check policies, procedures and records for objective evidence that requirements are being met, and will ask for specific details and speak to a variety of staff.

After the audit, the auditor will require some quiet time to write up evidence and collate details of non-conformities, in preparation for the closing meeting with the company, where the audit is summed up and details of the findings, including non-conformities, are given.

5   Unannounced Audits – Is There Anything Different?

The option to undertake the unannounced audit scheme provides companies with an opportunity to demonstrate their confidence in their systems and procedures, to the extent that they are willing to subject these to unannounced scrutiny. Companies may thereby gain a competitive advantage with their customers, who are given an opportunity to review suppliers' risk ratings. Customers may view suppliers in the unannounced audit scheme more favourably, depending on performance, and they may reduce the frequency of their own customer audits as a result.

The unannounced audit scheme is voluntary and the decision to participate in the scheme rests with the certificated company; however, the scheme is open only to those sites that are currently awarded a certification grade A+, A, B+ or B. To opt into the scheme, companies must notify their Certification Body of their intention within the first 3 months following a qualifying audit; after this period only the announced scheme will be available.

The grading criteria will be as for the normal audit. Successful completion of the audit will result in the awarding of certification grade A+, B+ or C+, where + indicates an unannounced audit, and this grade will appear on the certificate. This certificate will supersede the existing certificate.

The decision to opt into or out of the unannounced audit must be made after each subsequent audit, on an ongoing basis. If the company requests withdrawal from the programme, this should be within the first 6 months of the cycle. (In theory, the company will be expecting its next unannounced audit between months 6 and 12.) The next audit will then be announced and will occur within the 28 days up to and including the anniversary of the last audit. (This ensures that the maximum time between audits is not more than a year.)

Whilst it may be accepted that the company would need to ensure that arrangements such as facilities to undertake meetings and review documentation are made available at short notice, an unannounced audit should not affect the logistics of how an audit is undertaken, and should be approached in the same way by auditor and company.

The company should consider the requirements for contingency plans in the event of documents, such as personnel records, being kept in locked cupboards and the nominated key holder being off-site (e.g. through the provision of spare keys).

The validity of the current certificate ceases following the unannounced audit, so the certified status of the company will be revoked if the auditor is not permitted access to carry out the unannounced audit on arrival at a site.

Issue 6 of the *Global Standard for Food Safety* provides two options for unannounced audits:

Option 1: Full unannounced audit

■   This option is generally unchanged from Issue 5.

■   A number of days (up to 15) may be blocked out from the plan as non-audit days, to accommodate dates where an audit would be inappropriate.

- ◼ The audit will be unannounced and, although it can occur at any stage between months 3 and 12 of the audit due date, it shall typically be within the last 4 months of the certification cycle.

- ◼ The audit will be a full audit, examining all aspects of the supplier's systems against the requirements of the Standard.

Option 2: Two-part unannounced audit

- ◼ This option divides the audit process into two separate audits. The first audit is carried out as an unannounced audit and looks predominantly at items considered to be factory-based GMPs. The second audit is an announced audit and is predominantly a review of documentation and records. The latter visit can, therefore, be planned to ensure that the appropriate management staff are available to retrieve and discuss the records. The Requirements section of the Standard is colour-coded to identify the requirements that would be audited during the different visits.

- ◼ The Option 2 programme allows for a number of days (up to 10) to be blocked out from the plan as non-audit days, to accommodate dates where an audit would be inappropriate.

- ◼ The unannounced part of the audit can occur at any stage between months 6 and 10 of the audit cycle. (This is to allow the site time to correct any non-conformities and to enable these to be reviewed during the second part of the audit.) The announced part of the audit shall be planned to occur in the 28 days up to and including the anniversary of the last audit date.

6   Explanation of Terms

6.1   Colour coding of requirements

The clauses within the Standard have been colour coded to provide a guide to which requirements would usually be audited as part of the assessment of the site's production areas and facilities (i.e. the auditing of factory GMPs).

6.2   Fundamental requirements

The Standard contains certain requirements that have been designated as 'fundamental' requirements. These fundamental requirements relate to systems that are crucial to the establishment and operation of an effective food quality and safety operation. Ten requirements have been identified as 'fundamental' and are highlighted within the guidelines with the following symbol: ✿.

A fundamental requirement relates to a system that is well established, and that is continuously maintained and monitored by the company (as the absence of, or poor adherence to, this system would have serious repercussions on the integrity and safety of the product supplied). Although it depends on various factors, 'well established' generally means in operation for at least 3 months. For example, where a new facility has been built, a certification audit should not be invited before this time period to allow sufficient records to be available for review. 'Continuously maintained and monitored' means that evidence is provided that the controls necessary to meet the fundamental requirement are applied rigorously, and at the appropriate frequency. Fundamental requirements apply to those controls that cannot be implemented quickly prior to an audit (e.g. management commitment, internal audits) and where the output of their implementation can be assessed. They are designed to ensure that the quality system will be effective between certification dates.

A lack of focus on a fundamental requirement may result in certification not being granted.

6.3   'Shall' versus 'may'

The style of the Standard is generally one of guidance, to allow companies to ensure that all aspects of control have been considered, so that thorough and comprehensive policies and procedures may be developed. In some instances the Standard requires that criteria *must* be included within a policy or procedure, and this is generally covered by the term 'shall'. If any of the points included are not covered adequately, a non-conformity will result.

However, there are also a number of clauses that provide examples or guidelines, generally preceded by the words 'may include' or 'should'. This information is provided as guidance for incorporation in company policies and procedures. It is the responsibility of the company to ensure that the auditor is satisfied that the system in place is appropriate.

For example, clause 3.11.1:

> 'The company **shall** have documented procedures designed to report and effectively manage incidents and potential emergency situations that impact food safety, legality or quality. This **shall include** consideration of contingency plans to maintain business continuity. Incidents **may include**...'

6.4   Risk assessment

A number of clauses within the Standard refer to risk assessments being the basis for developing appropriate control procedures, such as establishing a frequency for monitoring a control point. Risk assessment is defined as using judgement to identify hazards and determine their impact on food safety, legality or quality, and designing an appropriate control or procedure to minimise the risk of problems occurring.

During the course of the certification audit, the auditor will require evidence of these risk assessments. For example, these may take the form of documents that identify the hazard, the risk of it occurring and the options for control; alternatively, this may be incorporated within established procedures. Risk assessments do not need to be long, complicated documents; they must, however, demonstrate which aspects have been assessed and, where further action has not been identified, some description of the justification will be required.

The principle is to demonstrate that any potential hazards have been considered by the company, and that the controls applied are justified and will stand up to robust challenge by any auditor. In many cases, industry best practice, where known and available, will meet this requirement.

6.5   Appropriate

A number of clauses within the Standard refer to the need to fulfil requirements 'where appropriate'. 'Appropriate' is defined as suitable for a particular condition or occasion, and requirements shall be met where it is an industry requirement or justified to do so.

A number of the requirements specify appropriate timescales, appropriate personnel, etc., and thus contain a level of judgement. They are designed to provide a degree of flexibility to ensure the operation of policies or procedures that are right for the organisation.

6.6   Documented procedures

In many instances, the Standard specifically states that requirements shall be satisfied by documented procedures; in others, this is implied as the company needs to demonstrate that systems are in place. Any policies and documents must be written in sufficient detail to satisfy their purpose and must reflect the activities that happen in practice. An example of a documented procedure and record form is given in Appendix 5.

6.7   Validation

Validation is defined as obtaining evidence that a control measure (or combination of measures), if properly implemented, is capable of controlling a hazard to a specified outcome. Validation activity is completed before the controls are introduced or when changes are expected (for example, new products, new processes or new equipment). Validation might include:

- document and data review – previous test results, industry data, codes of practice and legislation may all contain useful information

- experiments/testing – consider tests on the product or factory environment that will demonstrate control (worst-case-scenario tests, final product tests, etc.)

- challenge studies – for example, microbiological tests to establish whether a micro-organism of concern can grow in the product using the relevant time/conditions

- modelling – a number of predictive tools are available.

Several worked examples of validation can be found in Codex Guideline CAC/GL 69-2008, available at www.codexalimentarius.net/standard_list.jsp

6.8   Verification

Verification is defined as obtaining evidence, on a predetermined and ongoing basis, that a control is operating within the correct parameters. Verification requires the application of methods, procedures, tests or evaluations, in addition to monitoring, to determine whether the control measure is operating as intended. Verification activities may include:

- audits – both internal and third party

- review of records (e.g. records of the monitoring of temperatures and times, or other records completed during production)

- corrective action review

- test results – depending on the control being verified, these might include final products, raw materials, swabs, rapid tests, etc.

6.9   Monitoring

Monitoring is defined as conducting a planned sequence of observations or measurements to assess whether a control measure is within acceptable limits (for example, temperature checks, metal detector checks, test weights, etc.).

7   Format of Guidelines

Each clause of the Standard begins with a highlighted paragraph in bold text, 'the statement of intent', that all companies must comply with in order to gain certification. This statement of intent has been included within these guidelines.

Thereafter follows guidance on the requirement clauses, and the policies and processes to be put in place to ensure they are adequately fulfilled.

The numbering within Section II mirrors that within the Standard.

An explanation of the processes following the on-site audit is included in Section III.

SECTION II

REQUIREMENTS GUIDELINES

Section II

Requirements Guidelines

 Senior Management Commitment

1.1   Senior management commitment and continual improvement

FUNDAMENTAL

 The company's senior management shall demonstrate they are fully committed to the implementation of the requirements of the *Global Standard for Food Safety* and to processes which facilitate continual improvement of food safety and quality management.

Adoption and successful implementation of the Standard requires the commitment of senior management to ensure that food safety is part of the culture of the organisation and that support and resources are available. Without this commitment, it is very unlikely that the Standard could be applied consistently or the assurance that certification provides for customers could be honoured. There are requirements within the Standard which need to be understood and applied by most functions within the organisation, from purchasing to personnel and from maintenance to production. Experience has shown that only where the most senior management are committed to the process can this level of involvement be achieved consistently.

1.1.1   Documented policy

A policy that clearly states the overall aims to meet customer requirements, including the provision of safe, quality food, shows the intent of the company, so that all staff can work towards this common goal. This establishes the commitment of the company's senior management. The policy needs to be signed or endorsed by the person with overall responsibility for the actual site, to demonstrate the commitment at site level. Where the policy statement is a group policy statement, the site manager should endorse this – for instance, by countersigning the statement.

The policy statement only needs to be a summary and would usually be expressed in a single page. The policy statement must be current. Whilst it need not be dated, it must be updated when policies or senior management change.

The auditor will expect to see that the policy statement is communicated to staff. This may be through display on notice boards, inclusion in the induction process or availability on a company intranet. The policy applies to all staff, including temporary and contracted staff, and the method(s) of communication must be able to reach all such staff. Consideration should be given to providing the policy in appropriate languages – either written or oral – where non-native-speaking staff are employed.

1.1.2   Objectives

Senior management must set objectives concerning food safety and quality which help to achieve the stated policy. The objectives must have targets which ensure continuous improvement and these must be communicated so that the relevant staff understand what is required from them. The setting of these objectives also enables the allocation of suitable budgets and resources. Auditors will look for evidence that this has been done and communicated to the appropriate staff. For example, objectives may include:

- reducing consumer complaints

- fewer non-conforming products
- reduction in audit failures – both internal and external
- reduction in customer rejections or returns.

There are many other objectives that could be included here.

In each case, the objective must be measurable and documented, so that it is possible to review progress. Progress against targets shall be reviewed and reported to senior management at least quarterly. It may, for instance, be included in management meetings, or it may be the subject of a separate review or included in a report to management. Auditors will look for documented evidence of the quarterly progress review.

1.1.3   Management review

The purpose of the management review meeting is to take an overview of the food safety systems: what has been achieved, progress against objectives and the identification of targets and areas for improvement in the coming year.

Senior management are considered to be managers who have the authority to make decisions on food safety objectives and/or the provision of adequate human and financial resources. This would usually include the site manager and managers responsible for production, technical, purchasing, engineering and human resources. For large multi-site organisations this may include head-office personnel but should be driven by the senior management on site.

The auditor will be looking for evidence that, for each agenda item, sufficient information has been provided to allow an informed discussion leading to appropriate action plans to allow continuous improvement. This may be demonstrated through a review of the inputs to the meeting for each agenda item, minutes of the discussion of the item and, where necessary, agreed action plans.

For example, to demonstrate that the senior management have reviewed the management of the Hazard Analysis Critical Control Point (HACCP) system, the minutes should contain a general summary of the HACCP review meeting and a record of the outcomes of the HACCP meeting (meeting input), together with any actions requested during the senior management meeting (output of the management review).

The Standard identifies specific agenda items which shall be included within the meeting; however, additional relevant subjects can also be included.

For example, the agenda item on internal audits: the food safety system and Standard requirements should have been reviewed as part of the internal audit throughout the preceding year. Individual issues should have been identified and acted upon at the time and, where necessary, escalated up the management team. The input to the annual management review may be a summary of each internal audit in terms of the number of non-conformities, outstanding issues, a report on the key trends identified and underlying root cause(s), and suggestions for improvement. This allows a discussion and, where necessary, enables an action plan to be set for the next year (for example, a change in the frequency of auditing particular areas, training needs or the introduction of new targets).

One of the outputs from the meeting is a review of performance against the defined objectives (clause 1.1.2) and the establishment of new or amended targets and objectives for the following year. This should be clearly documented within the minutes of the meeting.

The outcomes from the review meeting must be communicated to relevant staff to ensure implementation. It should be evident to the auditor how this has been achieved (for instance, cascaded through staff briefings, use of notice boards, etc.).

Where timescales have been attributed to actions, it should be evident that this is followed up and the actions are completed within the timescale.

1.1.4   Management meetings

The objective of this clause is to ensure that there is a channel for food safety and quality issues to be raised and discussed at a management level within the business. Most businesses have weekly or monthly management meetings and the inclusion of safety, legality and quality as an agenda item within this meeting meets the requirements of this clause. The minutes for such meetings should demonstrate the discussion of food safety issues.

A schedule for the meetings needs to be in place.

1.1.5   Resources

Sites must have sufficient financial and human resources to be able to maintain the food safety systems and produce safe food in order to achieve certification.

Whilst a review of resources forms part of the management review process (clause 1.1.3), this will also be assessed by the auditor on the basis of the type, number and root cause of non-conformities identified at the audit.

The ability of the company to meet the requirements of the Standard will partly demonstrate that the appropriate resources and skills are available.

Where external consultants are used as the main source of technical knowledge, for example, it is essential that the company can demonstrate that the consultant is readily available and that there is no compromise of product safety and legality. It shall be ensured that day-to-day responsibilities are under the control of the company.

1.1.6   Provision of technical knowledge and information

Food safety issues and legislative requirements are constantly changing and the objective of this clause is to ensure that sites remain up to date, are able to meet legislation and adapt their food safety systems to protect against new threats. The company shall be able to demonstrate that it maintains up-to-date knowledge of relevant legislation, scientific and technical developments, and industry codes of practice. This may be achieved by:

- membership of a trade association which provides this service

- subscription to a service provider supplying legal updates

- help from government officials or local enforcement offices

- regular review of identified websites covering legislation and standards.

The company needs to demonstrate that it can readily access, either directly or through a third party, legislation relating to the product in the country, state or territory where the product is sold to the ultimate consumer.

The auditor will look for evidence of systematic checking and the process for ensuring the information is transferred into action as necessary.

Sites must understand and comply both with relevant food safety and labelling legislation in the country of manufacture and with any applicable legislation where the product can reasonably be expected to be sold.

1.1.7   Availability of a copy of the Standard

The Standard contains all of the requirements for compliance and certification details. This is the reference document required for certification and an official copy shall be available on each site in either paper or electronic version. The copyright for the Standard is owned by the BRC and the BRC does not permit the unauthorised copying of either the paper (official printed copy) or the electronic (pdf) version. Some sites choose to print one copy of the Standard from an electronic copy and this is acceptable.

A non-conformity will be recorded if the company does not meet this requirement.

1.1.8 Audit due dates

The audit due date is indicated on both the audit report and the certificate issued to all certificated sites. The responsibility for scheduling the next audit rests with the site. The audit may be taken in the 28 days up to and including the audit due date. Late audits are likely to result in a gap in certification and will result in the award of a major non-conformity unless exceptional circumstances occur as identified in the audit protocol, section 16.2. This includes situations where the site is:

■ situated in a specific country, state, territory or area where there is government advice not to visit, and there is no suitable local auditor

■ within a statutory exclusion zone that prevents access, e.g. an isolation zone for foot-and-mouth disease

■ in an area that has suffered a natural or unnatural disaster, rendering the site unable to produce or the auditor unable to visit.

Lack of personnel is not an acceptable reason for adjusting recertification audit dates; the smooth operation of the site is expected in the absence of individual managers, because of shared management responsibility, adequate deputisation and established systems of working. The undertaking of building work is also not an acceptable reason for delay unless the site is not in production whilst the building work is being carried out.

Where the site has opted into one of the unannounced audit schemes, it becomes the responsibility of the Certification Body to ensure the requirement is met.

1.1.9 Senior management attendance at the audit

The most senior operations managers on site, i.e. those who are responsible for the 'hands-on' daily running of the site, shall be present for at least the opening and closing meetings of the audit. It may be the case that the most senior operations managers within the company are absent on the day of the audit due to other commitments; however, there shall always be a nominated deputy available. The objective is to ensure that non-conformities are effectively understood and agreed, and that there is the authority to ensure these are corrected.

A major non-conformity will result if this requirement is not fully complied with.

1.1.10 Recurring non-conformities

Non-conformities identified in previous certification audits shall have been fully and effectively rectified and these will be checked during the current audit. Where the previous audit was carried out against Issue 6, the effective identification and correction of the root cause should prevent recurrence of the exact or similar non-conformities. A major or minor non-conformity against this clause may be raised if this is not the case, along with a non-conformity against the clause that has a recurring issue.

1.2 Organisational structure, responsibilities and management authority

> The company shall have a clear organisational structure and lines of communication to enable effective management of product safety, legality and quality.

The objective is to ensure it is clear to staff where responsibility for all aspects of the food safety and quality system rest and that the responsible person has the knowledge and ability to fulfil the role.

1.2.1 Organisational charts and assignment of responsibilities

This clause applies to managers and supervisors particularly.

An organisation chart shall be available, clearly indicating reporting lines for all senior management on the site and, where applicable, relationships to head-office roles. This shall be up to date. The chart would normally be expected to show both a position and the named person occupying that position. Where the chart shows job titles only, other documents must indicate the person occupying each position.

The chart needs to clearly indicate reporting relationships and responsibilities for staff of relevance to the management of food safety – for example, any laboratory staff, product development teams and quality assurance (QA) staff, as appropriate.

It must be clearly documented who is expected to deputise in the absence of a manager. This would usually be identified on the organisational chart and/or in job descriptions, but it could also be in the form of a table. The responsibilities may be assigned to either a more senior or a more junior person, so long as the deputy has the knowledge and ability to adequately cover for the absent manager's particular responsibility. Deputies may be appointed for the whole role or particular responsibilities may be deputised to different people, so long as this is clearly defined.

Responsibilities shall be defined for key aspects of the food safety and quality system, including, for example, decisions on corrective actions, non-conforming products, process deviations, finished product release, document control and customer complaints. It is usual for specific responsibilities to be defined within the job descriptions of key staff (management and supervisors) whose activities affect product safety, legality and quality. The specific responsibilities may, however, be described instead within procedures.

The auditor will be looking for both documented responsibilities and for evidence through discussion or practical application that the responsible person is able to fulfil the role.

1.2.2   Employee roles and responsibilities

The objective is to ensure that employees, including temporary staff and agency staff, are able to work effectively and ensure that food safety and quality is maintained. This will usually be established by the auditor discussing the employees' jobs with the employees themselves during the audit.

There is no requirement for a detailed job description. However, employees should be aware of their particular responsibilities and to whom concerns or issues affecting food safety should be reported.

Where the role or an activity which makes up part of the role covers a food safety issue described within a procedure (for example, a CCP or prerequisite programme), the employee must understand what is expected and be able to access the relevant procedure.

2 The Food Safety Plan – HACCP

FUNDAMENTAL

> The company shall have a fully implemented and effective food safety plan based on Codex Alimentarius HACCP principles.

2.1   The HACCP food safety team – Codex Alimentarius Step 1

For a comprehensive HACCP food safety plan to be established and maintained, it needs to be managed by a nominated team with the relevant skills and experience. The number of HACCP food safety team members needs to be appropriate to the size and structure of the company, as the team shall include representatives of each department with responsibility for operation of the Standard. There will always be more than one person, since a single person does not constitute a 'team'. The team needs knowledge of the types of operations that are carried out within the company and the hazards these operations may present to the product.

It is good practice to document the team members within the HACCP study, with a summary of their roles within the company. It needs to be ensured that the members of the HACCP food safety team are reviewed and maintained – for example, when job responsibilities change or personnel leave or join the company. Consideration should be given to members to establish and review the documentation and to champion these principles on a day-to-day basis within the production environment.

The HACCP food safety team leader shall be able to demonstrate competency in HACCP (through the quality of the plan) and through a knowledge of HACCP principles. Documented evidence of their qualification needs to be given, e.g. successful completion of an industry-recognised HACCP training course or extensive experience in implementing or training HACCP. The team leader may be an appropriately qualified external consultant or an internal staff member.

Training records need to demonstrate that adequate training has been given to all HACCP food safety team members. This may be achieved through either an external course or internal training. Where external expertise has been used in developing the HACCP plan, the site must demonstrate ownership of the requirements identified.

Senior management commitment is required to support the HACCP food safety team (clause 1). This may be demonstrated by the presence of senior management within the HACCP food safety team, policy statements referring to HACCP, or evidence within management review meetings that HACCP issues are discussed and reviewed. The results of the HACCP plan shall be demonstrated to be integrated into the food safety and quality management system.

2.2   Prerequisite programmes

Issue 6 has placed a greater requirement on the HACCP team to consider the prerequisite programme. These are the basic environmental and production conditions necessary for the production of safe food and the control of generic hazards. They are usually covered by day-to-day activities and form part of good manufacturing or hygiene practices.

The prerequisite programme needs to provide a solid base on which the HACCP system can be developed. It is therefore vital that the prerequisite programme works effectively. Later sections of the Standard provide further detail on some requirements for effective management of several of the specific prerequisite programmes identified, e.g. cleaning (4.11), pest control (4.13) and training (7.1).

Whilst it is expected that the prerequisite programme is effective in achieving the level of control required to ensure food safety, it is not a requirement that a documented validation of every prerequisite is undertaken. However, where a prerequisite is used to manage a specific hazard (for example, cleaning regimes used to prevent allergen cross-contamination) there needs to be documented validation that the prerequisite controls the identified hazard.

Prerequisites used to control specific hazards shall be subject to routine verification activity and records should detail the control measures and monitoring systems used.

Example validation and verification activities for cleaning to prevent allergen contamination are given in clause 5.2.8.

2.3   Describe the product – Codex Alimentarius Step 2

All products and processes shall be covered by appropriate HACCP plans. This may be achieved through a single HACCP plan covering a group of products with similar process characteristics, where it shall be demonstrated that product variations (e.g. pack type or degree of preparation) have been assessed. Alternatively, HACCP plans may be split into 'modules' which cover specific process steps and which can be used in a 'mix-and-match' structure to create an HACCP plan for any given product. The formation and completeness of the HACCP plan for specific products may be challenged during the audit. It shall be clear where the process starts and ends.

2.3.1   Product description

A full description of the product is required to ensure that all aspects that may affect food safety have been considered. The Standard gives guidance on the factors that shall be considered:

- composition (e.g. raw materials, ingredients, allergens, recipe)
- origin of ingredients (e.g. climatic conditions, culture or food safety standards may make some countries a greater risk than others)
- physical or chemical properties that impact food safety (e.g. pH, a_w)
- treatment and processing (e.g. cooking, cooling)
- packaging system (e.g. modified atmosphere, vacuum)
- storage and distribution conditions (e.g. chilled, ambient)
- target safe shelf-life under prescribed storage and usage conditions
- instructions for use, and potential for known customer misuse (e.g. storage, preparation).

The characteristics need to be documented. This may be within a product specification if it is cross-referenced and changes are identified to the HACCP team.

Product groups can be used where the products are similar (e.g. different pack sizes). These shall be linked to the HACCP flow diagrams. However, where specifically different products (e.g. coated and non-coated meat products) are manufactured these are to be treated as separate products or groups.

2.3.2   Sources of information

Up-to-date background information shall be taken into account when preparing the HACCP plan. It is necessary, therefore, that suitable information is collated and maintained.

There are many sources of information, particularly on the internet, e.g. CODEX, European Food Standards Agency, US Food and Drug Administration, Rapid Alert System for Food and Feed (RASFF). Sources of information shall be referenced in the HACCP plan and shall be recoverable/available on request (using an internet search engine to find the information during the audit is not acceptable).

A listing of legislation or codes of practice referenced may be helpful.

Many membership organisations provide useful information. Where membership information is referenced, this also needs to be available on site (either electronically or in hard copy).

The Standard lists, for guidance, some types of information that may be considered in developing the HACCP food safety plan:

- the latest scientific literature

- historical and known hazards associated with specific food products (good practice is to be as specific as possible, e.g. name the specific micro-organism(s) that are known hazards to the product, rather than just listing 'bacteria')

- relevant codes of practice

- recognised guidelines

- food safety legislation relevant for the production and sale of products in destination countries, states or territories

- customer requirements.

2.4 Identify intended use – Codex Alimentarius Step 3

The HACCP food safety team needs to consider and document the intended use of the products by the customer and the ultimate consumer to ensure that all risks have been assessed. For example, areas to consider are:

- target population (e.g. does this include high-risk groups such as infants, elderly people or allergy sufferers?)

- handling and preparation (e.g. will the product be consumed without further cooking?)

- customer supply chain

- storage (e.g. frozen, or the requirement for chilled storage following opening of the pack).

2.5 Construct a process flow diagram – Codex Alimentarius Step 4

An accurate flow diagram indicating all process steps, including all inputs and outputs, needs to be constructed. This may be achieved through one diagram or in a modular form as described in clause 2.3, but it shall clearly identify the interaction between process steps. The Standard lists guidance on the points to consider and include when developing the flow diagram:

- a plan of premises and equipment layout to facilitate consideration of cross-contamination risks (e.g. allergen control)

- raw materials, including introduction of utilities and other contact materials (e.g. water, packaging)

- sequence and interaction of all process steps (e.g. method of transportation between each step)

- outsourced processes and subcontracted work

- process parameters

- potential for process delay (i.e. how products or ingredients will be handled if a delay occurs)

- rework and recycling

- low/high-care/high-risk area segregation

- finished products, intermediate/semi-processed products, by-products and waste.

The flow diagrams shall be signed and dated.

2.6 Verify flow diagram – Codex Alimentarius Step 5

The flow diagram shall be verified as accurate. This verification shall be conducted whenever there is a review of the plan and at least once per year; signing and dating the approved flow diagram helps to demonstrate that this has been completed. An on-site member of the HACCP food safety team, part of or the whole team shall check that the flow diagram is accurate by a physical walk-through of the process within the production area. The auditor is likely to undertake part or all of the process during the audit, so any anomalies between the documented controls and what is seen in practice may highlight a non-conformity.

It is important that any daily or seasonal variations are considered during the verification process (for example, the production of a Christmas product range that uses ingredients or processes that are not used during the rest of the year).

2.7 List all potential hazards associated with each process step, conduct a hazard analysis and consider any measures to control identified hazards – Codex Alimentarius Step 6, Principle 1

The scope or terms of reference of the HACCP plan shall be confirmed, i.e. what hazards are considered and their potential to contaminate the product.

2.7.1 List of potential hazards

The process flow diagram is a useful tool in considering potential risks at each stage in the production of the products.

It is expected that the list shall include biological, chemical, allergen and physical hazards. These need to detail:

- specific micro-organisms (e.g. *E. coli, Salmonella*)
- specific chemicals (e.g. veterinary residues and pesticides)
- cleaning chemicals
- machinery lubricants
- types of foreign bodies (e.g. glass, metal, plastic)
- allergens (e.g. peanuts).

Consideration must be given to the sources of the potential hazards, which could include raw materials, processes, the factory environment, etc.

There shall be a description of each hazard and its sources – one hazard may have several potential sources. This is important to ensure that effective controls for each source of hazard are established.

2.7.2 Hazard analysis

Any hazards identified in clause 2.7.1 shall be evaluated against the criteria detailed in clause 2.7.2 of the Standard, considering the consequences of the identified hazard:

- likely occurrence of hazard
- severity of the effects on consumer safety
- vulnerability of those exposed
- survival and multiplication of micro-organisms of specific concern to the product
- presence or production of toxins, chemicals or foreign bodies
- contamination of raw materials, intermediate/semi-processed product or finished product.

Evidence of decisions shall be kept within the HACCP food safety plan.

There are a range of tools that may assist with the evaluation of hazards (for example, quadrant graphs, scoring systems, logic tables or decision trees). The team may choose to use these tools for consideration of this requirement. Such tools may also help in establishing critical control points (CCPs).

Where elimination of a hazard is not possible, acceptable levels for a hazard need to be defined. Reference should be made to legal requirements or scientific evidence to justify the acceptable levels – for example, microbiological standards or presence of mycotoxins.

2.7.3   Control measures

Control measures required to reduce or eliminate the identified hazards shall be established. Any hazard that cannot be eliminated shall have control measures designed to reduce it to an acceptable level of presence. This acceptable hazard level (e.g. setting a target of < 100 cfu/g of *Staphylococcus aureus* in finished product) needs to be justified. Industry guidelines, codes of practice, legislation, etc. can help to establish and justify these levels. Documentation for justification and the reasoning behind the levels shall be available.

Where control is achieved via the prerequisite programme, reference shall be made to the specific prerequisite that controls the hazard. Whilst it is expected that the prerequisite programme is effective in achieving the level of control required to control a hazard, it is not a requirement that a documented validation of every prerequisite is undertaken. As a guide, wherever a prerequisite programme has been used to control a specific hazard (for example, cleaning regimes used to prevent allergen cross-contamination), there needs to be documented validation that the prerequisite programme controls the identified hazard. Many prerequisites provide a more general, less specific control – for example, pest control or personnel hygiene requirements. In such instances, validation does not need to be documented but must be based on accepted best practices and any supplementary supporting scientific information that is available.

2.8   Determine the critical control points (CCPs) – Codex Alimentarius Step 7, Principle 2

Each control measure shall be considered to identify those that are critical. Records shall be available showing how this has been conducted and how decisions have been reached. The use of a two- or four-question decision tree may be useful, and where this has been used, a copy of the tree and the results of the questions shall be recorded. See Appendix 2 for an example of a decision tree. Modification of a process may be necessary to ensure that a suitable control can be employed.

2.9   Establish critical limits for each CCP – Codex Alimentarius Step 8, Principle 3

Having identified all the relevant CCPs, the HACCP team shall then identify critical limits. The critical limit is the point that separates safe product from unsafe or acceptable from unacceptable.

Some critical limits are defined in legislation; however, many will require experimental results or the advice of appropriate industry specialists.

2.9.1   Critical limits

All identified CCPs shall have defined critical limits. Criteria often used include measurements of temperature, time, moisture level, pH and a_w, and sensory parameters such as visual appearance and texture. Details on how critical limits have been reached shall be documented – this may include industry best practice, legislation or validation studies undertaken by the company.

Where critical limits are based on subjective data such as visual appearance or texture, they need to be supported by clear guidance or examples. This may include the provision of examples to staff at process control points, including photographs of acceptable and unacceptable limits. It may also include product samples for comparison.

2.9.2   Validation and documentation of critical limits

Documented evidence shall be available, showing how the control measures at CCPs have been validated to ensure that they control, reduce or eliminate the hazard to the specified critical limit. Validation must demonstrate that if the control measures are followed as specified, and the critical limits fulfilled (at minimum and maximum levels, where a range is specified), a consistently safe product will be produced. Evidence could come from professional bodies, trade associations, historical processing data, scientific or technical literature, or legislation. In addition, scientifically valid experimental or pilot plant trial data may be required. Additional exercises, such as challenge testing, may be used as a validation tool to confirm the capability of the process.

Example: Data establishing the log reduction of a specified pathogen, measured by laboratory testing of food samples following thermal processing.

Further information on completing validation can be obtained from Codex guideline CAG/GL 69-2008. This can be downloaded from www.codexalimentarius.net/standard_list.jsp.

2.10 Establish a monitoring system for each CCP – Codex Alimentarius Step 9, Principle 4

Monitoring is a planned set of checks or measurements for each CCP to ensure it is consistently meeting the identified critical limit. Monitoring must be recorded in terms of both the procedures to be followed and the results obtained.

2.10.1 Monitoring system

Each CCP needs to be monitored to ensure that the established limits are not exceeded. This can be achieved by observing or measuring the CCP at scheduled intervals.

A monitoring procedure shall be established for each CCP. As a minimum, this procedure needs to indicate:

- the CCP to which the procedure relates
- staff (or staff role) responsible for monitoring the CCP
- training requirements for responsible staff
- frequency at which the monitoring is completed
- instruction on how the monitoring is completed
- the requirements for record keeping (clause 2.10.2).

Monitoring shall be able to detect variation, which may result in limits being broken if no remedial action is taken. It shall be at a sufficient frequency to ensure that any necessary remedial action can be taken in sufficient time so that it does not constitute a risk to the product and ensures that no potentially affected product has been released for sale or dispatch to the customer. Methods used may include online or offline measurements and may be continuous or discontinuous.

2.10.2 Monitoring system records

Staff shall be nominated to undertake the monitoring and shall be suitably trained.

The results of monitoring activities shall be recorded. As a minimum, these records shall include:

- date and time
- result
- signature of the individual completing the monitoring
- where appropriate, the signature of the individual (e.g. the line manager) verifying the record (depending on the working practices in the factory, it may be appropriate to complete verification at identified points during the day, e.g. at end of shift).

Records shall include action taken when monitoring indicates loss of control.

Where records are in electronic form the site shall be able to demonstrate that the records have been checked and verified. For example, an electronic signature could be added, a record form could be completed, or the records could be printed, signed and dated.

2.11   Establish a corrective action plan – Codex Alimentarius Step 10, Principle 5

A documented procedure needs to be established, detailing the actions to be taken when monitoring indicates that limits have been exceeded or may be exceeded if no remedial action is taken.

The procedure shall include:

- authorised personnel (i.e. who is authorised to make decisions about product produced where limits have been exceeded and the corrective actions to be taken)

- immediate remedial action to be taken

- quarantine procedures to manage products that have passed through the process and may have exceeded the limits, e.g. products that have been metal detected since the last satisfactory metal detector check

- disposal procedures for unsafe products

- additional actions that may be required – for example, alternative processing, increased monitoring, etc.

The corrective action plan needs to include how any product that may be in breach of the established limits is handled and/or stored until its safety status is established. The handling and storage procedure must ensure that implicated product cannot enter production or be distributed to customers unless confirmed safe and released by the authorised staff.

2.12   Establish verification procedures – Codex Alimentarius Step 11, Principle 6

The HACCP plan, including controls managed by prerequisites, shall be verified to ensure that it is effective. Verification requires objective evidence that the specified requirements are being met. The Standard gives the following guidance on what to include in verification studies:

- internal audits

- review of records where acceptable limits have been exceeded

- review of complaints by enforcement authorities or customers

- review of incidents of product withdrawal or recall.

These give information about how, when and how often the system has potentially not been under control. Actions and procedures specified in the HACCP plan shall match procedures and work instructions in use. It shall be ensured that frequencies stated on work instructions match those in the HACCP plan.

The results of this verification step shall be documented and communicated to the HACCP food safety team members as part of the review process.

2.13   HACCP documentation and record keeping – Codex Alimentarius Step 12, Principle 7

Records shall be kept to demonstrate that the HACCP food safety plan, including hazards controlled by prerequisite programmes, is fully implemented. This shall include all steps in creating and reviewing the plan, records of control and monitoring procedures, training records of staff, etc.

2.14   Review the HACCP plan

The HACCP food safety plan and associated prerequisite programmes shall be reviewed on a regular basis – as a minimum, once per year. A review of some or all of the HACCP is required in response to changes in the following:

- raw materials or supplier of raw materials
- ingredients or recipe
- processing methods and equipment
- packaging, storage or distribution conditions
- consumer use
- new product design and development
- emergence of a new risk – for example, adulteration of an ingredient
- developments in scientific information related to ingredients, process or product.

Changes that may affect product safety, such as those listed in the Standard, need to be evaluated in the context of the HACCP plan before they are introduced, and the HACCP plan amended as necessary. This may be achieved by documenting a procedure that lists the activities or changes that shall trigger a HACCP review, but this shall be backed by evidence that the review has actually been carried out.

It is expected that the HACCP food safety plan is reviewed at least once a year, even if there have been no changes to the product range or processing methods.

3   Food Safety and Quality Management System

3.1   Food safety and quality manual

> The company's processes and procedures to meet the requirements of this Standard shall be documented to allow consistent application, facilitate training, and support due diligence in the production of a safe product.

A well documented, systematic management system forms the basis for the product and process controls necessary to produce safe products, meet customer specifications and enable staff to be trained and informed.

3.1.1   The food safety and quality manual

Policies, procedures and work instructions must be in place, easily retrievable and available where needed, and must cover the requirements of the Standard. These documents shall be collated into one or more quality manuals which form the reference point for all of the documents included in the quality system.

These documents may exist on paper, i.e. 'hard copy', or may be controlled on an electronic system.

In a small, simple operation, the manual may contain the majority of the procedures controlling the processes. In a complex operation, it may contain the headline policies and reference where more detailed operating instructions can be found.

The manual should include an overview of how the company's policies and procedures are organised. This organisation must be understood by those using the documents and easily demonstrated.

Where the site is part of a company governed by a head office, the interaction between the site's documented system and that of other sites and the head office should be clear. All policies and procedures necessary for the operation of the site being assessed must be available at that site.

There is *no* requirement for sites to have a quality manual which is numbered in accordance with the BRC Standard numbering system.

3.1.2   Availability of manual to staff

The objective of this requirement is to ensure that key staff have access to up-to-date policies and procedures at all times and in the most appropriate format. For example, the incident management procedure should be available to the relevant team members via internet link or other off-site format.

Staff needing such documents as part of their role within the company shall always have access to them.

The procedures documented in the manual will be evaluated against the actual practices on the site, with the expectation that they are followed correctly.

3.1.3   Clear procedures and work instructions for staff

Procedures and work instructions shall be documented in a clear and unambiguous format.

Anyone using an authorised document shall be able to understand its relevance, what the document is for and how to use it. Evidence is required to demonstrate clear understanding of procedures by staff, as this will be challenged by the auditor.

Consideration may be given to providing the policy in appropriate languages – either written or oral – to ensure that staff understand the policy and the role that individuals play in achieving these objectives. Where translations are used, a record should be kept of who translated the information, into which language(s). Both translator and recipient staff should sign the training record indicating that the translated version has been understood.

Documentation shall include the use of photographs, diagrams or other pictorial instructions where written communication alone is not sufficient.

For example, diagrams added to cleaning instructions can give clarity on pieces of equipment to remove or focus on. The use of signs and pictures can be particularly useful for communicating personal hygiene and protective clothing requirements.

3.2   Documentation control

> The company shall operate an effective document control system to ensure that only the correct versions of documents, including recording forms, are available and in use.

Documents shall be effectively controlled to ensure that staff are working with the most up-to-date information and to minimise the potential for mistakes. Documents include policies, procedures, work instructions, records, forms, specifications, data lists, etc. and information that is written down and defined. They may be available as 'hard copy' (i.e. on paper) or in electronic format.

Key documents found to be in use during the audit and which are not properly authorised or of the correct version may lead to a non-conformity.

3.2.1   Document management system

All documents in use need to be properly authorised and must be the correct version.

The Standard requires that the site has a documented procedure which describes the method by which documents are controlled and managed. The procedure needs to include instructions on how the following features of the document control system are controlled:

- responsibilities for the management of the system
- the list of all controlled documents, indicating the current version number and the allocation of controlled copies of the document (see below)
- identification of controlled documents (e.g. document ID, issue date, version number)
- records of the reason for any change(s) (see below)
- method of rescinding and replacing documents.

In order to demonstrate the control of document issue, it is necessary to maintain a register of all controlled documents, their allocation and issue status. Where the controlled documents are all contained on an electronic system, it is usual for printed versions to be marked as uncontrolled. Each copy shall be authorised (e.g. with a signature or stamp) to show it is for use, and each shall be given a version number so that out-of-date documents can be identified and removed. This shall be evidenced by the fact that all documents in use are the most up-to-date version.

When a document is changed, a record needs to be made of the change and the reason for the change. This can be achieved by keeping a copy of the previous version with the reason for change written on it, or by keeping a history of amendments log. Consideration should also be given to the most effective method of communicating the changes to staff – for instance, by highlighting the change within the new document.

3.3   Record completion and maintenance

> The company shall maintain genuine records to demonstrate the effective control of product safety, legality and quality.

Records are the documents that contain details providing permanent evidence of information about past events – particularly events concerning product safety, quality and legality. Records shall therefore be maintained in an appropriate way to ensure they demonstrate control of systems and operations.

3.3.1   Record completion

Records shall be legible and genuine. For example, they shall be completed at the time of checks (i.e. not before or after) and shall be completed in an appropriate manner, e.g. using a pen (pencil can be altered after the event). Records shall be appropriately authorised; this may include the initials or signature of the operator or supervisor verifying the records.

Any alterations to records need to be justified and authorised. A suitable procedure shall be in place to manage any mistakes that are made, e.g. neatly crossing through the 'inaccurate' information, noting the reason for the error and giving the initials of the person making the change. Note that the use of correction fluid/'white out' is not acceptable.

Records shall be retrievable when required, e.g. during an audit or during the investigation of a customer complaint. They shall be maintained and stored in a manner that will enable them to be retrieved when required – for example, being appropriately filed by date or reference number and in such a way that they are still legible within the specified storage timeframe. Consideration should be given to the potential for degradation during storage (for example, due to ink fading, degradation of thermal paper or breakdown of electronic media).

Records must be created in such a manner that they accurately transmit the intended information (e.g. can be read by others and are traceable to the creator of the record via initials or signature).

Electronic records need to be similarly controlled, and therefore a documented system needs to be in place to authorise access and amending of these systems. Electronic documents shall be suitably backed up to prevent loss. Consideration should be given to testing electronic retrieval systems and records of these tests should be retained.

3.3.2   Record storage

The retention time for records shall be established by the company, and procedures put in place for appropriate handling, so that records are retained in good condition for this period and are retrievable.

Records that may be called upon to demonstrate the integrity or legality of the product must be kept for a period not less than the indicated shelf life plus one year. Additional retention time may be required by legislation, by customers or due to the nature of the product (for example, extension beyond the normal shelf life by customer freezing). As records may be called upon by a customer as part of a legal defence, consideration should be given to the length of time that may pass from production of a product to notification of impending legal action in the country of sale.

Where products have an undefined shelf life (for instance, some wines and alcoholic drinks), the company should define a reasonable record retention period based on experience of customer usage, time for complaints to be notified and any legal precedents. It would be usual for records to be kept for at least 3 years in such situations.

Any legal requirements specifying how long documents shall be retained will be complied with. Similarly, if customers have any specific requirements for record retention times, these shall be observed.

3.4   Internal audit

FUNDAMENTAL

 The company shall be able to demonstrate it verifies the effective application of the food safety plan and the implementation of the requirements of the *Global Standard for Food Safety.*

Internal auditing is a key factor in ensuring continued compliance with the requirements of the Standard, and shall be regarded by the management of the company as being critical to its operation. Internal audits demonstrate whether control systems are working correctly and effectively, and identify areas for improvement. Internal auditing forms part of the verification of systems, a crucial step within the control of the HACCP food safety plan. Therefore, this requirement is fundamental.

3.4.1   Internal audit programme

The scope of internal audits needs to be established but shall ensure that all aspects of the food safety and quality system, including the HACCP programme, prerequisite programmes, policies, documentation, hygiene and production, are audited.

The site shall evaluate the risk inherent in each section and determine the frequency of audits accordingly. For example, the site should consider the severity of consequences if the system, or compliance with it, is inadequate, and the potential for changes that would affect these control systems. Frequency may also be influenced by known issues within the company, best practice or customer requirements. All activities shall be covered at least annually. However, it is recommended that individual sections of the process, documentation or production are scheduled for different audit dates throughout the year. The internal audit should examine processes in detail by taking documented procedures and work instructions and comparing these against actual working practices. The use of a checklist covering the BRC Standard requirements may be of value in preparing for an audit, but this is very unlikely to fulfil the depth of internal auditing requirements expected in the Standard.

3.4.2   Auditor training and independence

Auditing is an acquired skill and auditors need to be trained to ensure they are carrying out this function effectively. Training shall include auditing skills, as well as relevant technical knowledge of the activity to be audited, such as HACCP or appropriate product technical knowledge. Internal auditors shall be able to show via training records (clause 7.1.4) that they have received formal training on internal auditing, either via attendance at an external course or via training within the company. During the audit, the auditor may also discuss the process with internal auditors to establish their level of competence.

Internal auditors shall be independent of the process being audited. For example, it is not acceptable for workers on one shift to audit the work of another shift completing the same work, as they are not independent of the operation. This is to ensure that the audit is rigorous and thorough, and that work needed to make corrections or improvements can be identified by an auditor who is not biased or influenced by working in the area. The use of external auditors may need to be considered if internal resources are insufficient. Note that training records for external personnel shall be available.

3.4.3   Internal audit records and corrective actions

Audit results must be documented, clearly indicating what was audited. Reports shall show evidence of conformity as well as non-conformity, and therefore tick lists showing that items have been assessed will not normally be acceptable as the only form of evidence. Information showing how the items audited have fulfilled the requirements, or how they are non-compliant, is required.

Notes, references or copies shall be kept as evidence of aspects that have been examined, to allow an independent reviewer to reach the same conclusion as the internal auditor. For example, the date and title of records that were inspected should be noted in sufficient detail to allow them to be traced; if any records are non-compliant, precise detail of the non-compliance should be given. The listing of records reviewed can also ensure that a wide range of records are reviewed, e.g. training records of a variety of staff, rather than repeated audits of the same records. Records will also confirm whether anything has changed since the last audit.

The results of audits need to be communicated to relevant staff, and corrective actions and timescales agreed. This may be achieved via operational or review meetings, or via an update at the end of the audit combined with documentation such as a memo or a copy of the audit report. Responsibility for corrective actions shall be demonstrated – for example, by being recorded on the audit record sheet.

Where non-conformities have been identified, it shall be verified that corrective action has been completed effectively. Good practice would ensure that a nominated member of staff with the appropriate authority checks that the action has been taken within the agreed timescale, and that this has rectified the problem sufficiently to prevent recurrence. The nominated staff member should not be the person responsible for completion of the actions, and should ideally be the original auditor.

Full records of all internal audits and the results, including conformity and non-conformity and verification of corrective actions, shall be kept for a defined period, typically 2 years.

3.4.4   Documented inspections

The Standard requires a programme of documented inspections to ensure that the factory environment and processing equipment are maintained in a suitable condition. These inspections are different from the internal audit programme specified in clauses 3.4.1–3.4.3, which examines practices against documented procedures. These hygiene- and fabrication-based inspections assess standards of cleaning, equipment, building fabrication and personal hygiene to ensure that high standards are maintained and a safe, hygienic production environment is in place.

The frequency of the inspections should be based on risk. For open product areas, inspections need to be at least monthly. Inspections in high-care and high-risk areas could be daily or weekly.

Line start-up checks, which may occur daily or at shift changes in many operations, can form part of this inspection programme.

Individuals responsible for completing these inspections should be suitably trained for the systems they are checking. The absolute requirements for independence identified in clause 3.4.2 do not always apply to these inspections; for instance, it would be acceptable for line start-up checks to be carried out by line supervisors or managers. External agencies may be used to carry out inspections.

It is important that issues identified at the inspections are corrected as soon as possible and always such that product risk is minimised. The records of the inspections and corrective actions shall be retained and consideration should be given to using the inspections to identify trends and drive improvements through, for example, the use of scored inspection results.

3.5   Supplier and raw material approval and performance monitoring

3.5.1   Management of suppliers of raw materials and packaging

> The company shall have an effective supplier approval and monitoring system to ensure that any potential risks from raw materials (including packaging) to the safety, legality and quality of the final product are understood and managed.

All materials brought onto the site to become part of the final product (including product packaging) must be sourced through approved suppliers and monitored. This approval process and programme for monitoring raw materials will consider the potential risk the material represents (in terms of safety, legality and quality).

The system shall consist of an initial approval process and an ongoing monitoring process.

The risk assessment process should help to focus increased attention on those raw materials or suppliers presenting greater risk.

3.5.1.1 Raw material risk assessment

All proposed ingredients shall be subjected to a documented assessment of their inherent risk. This may form part of the HACCP plan; however, as this is an important starting point for the production of safe food, it needs to be detailed and will be assessed specifically by the auditor. The assessment may be of individual products or, where a number of raw materials share the same characteristics and likely risks, these may be grouped together. When grouping materials, each should also be considered to ensure that it does not have a particular risk factor. For example, in a bakery, all dried fruit may be considered of similar risk for assessment. Risk may vary between factories, however, due to a different overall effect on quality. In a bakery, where flour is a critical ingredient, it may be necessary to consider each flour separately (e.g. white, granary, wholemeal, etc.), whereas other sites may group all types of flour together.

This risk assessment should consider:

- known hazards associated with the ingredient provided or components of it (examples of hazards include aflatoxins in nuts and cereals, histamine in fish, pesticide residues in products of plant origin, *Salmonella* in dried foods such as milk powder, *Listeria* in chilled foods, etc. Access to reference information and an awareness of emerging food issues is essential to ensure all known risks are assessed)

- use of the ingredient (for example, an ingredient added following a final kill step may present a different risk from an ingredient added at the beginning of a process)

- spread of ingredient in the company/final products

- nature of the supplier

- historical evidence of the supplier and raw material

- geographic origins (products from particular origins may carry a greater risk because of more relaxed local legal requirements or a less developed food safety culture)

- methods of manufacture (for example, if a site is using pineapple as an ingredient, the risk will depend on whether fresh pineapple or canned pineapple is used)

- significance of the ingredient to the final product (for example, some 'safe' ingredients, such as flour in bread making, may be fundamental to the performance of the product and therefore require higher levels of control to ensure consistent quality)

- customer or legislative requirements (for example, suppliers may be specified by customers, but this does not negate the need for risk assessment).

The risk assessment shall consider the potential for:

- allergen contamination

- foreign-body risks

- microbiological contamination

- chemical contamination.

Additional focus shall be placed on raw materials where claims are being made for the final product (e.g. organic or suitable for allergy sufferers) or where there is microbiological risk from components added after heat treatment. Suppliers and their control systems must be assessed robustly to ensure compliance with the requirements.

Where different departments are involved in the process (for example, head office or different sections of the site technical team), there needs to be a linked process to demonstrate the responsibilities of each team and how these work together to operate the system.

The outcome of this activity shall also be considered when assessing the requirements for supplier approval and for monitoring and acceptance procedures (clauses 3.5.1.2 and 3.5.2).

3.5.1.2   Documented supplier approval and monitoring system

All suppliers shall be evaluated for their ability to meet the specifications of the materials they are supplying and requirements for safety, quality and legality.

The company shall document its procedure for supplier approval and monitoring. This needs to include the methods of approval, frequency of monitoring, responsibilities and how the process will be managed.

Approval could include a range of activities, such as a combination of the following:

- successful site audit by an appropriately qualified auditor
- third-party certification scheme, such as the Global Standards for food, packaging, or storage and distribution
- completion of a company questionnaire.

The choice of approval and ongoing monitoring process for any given supplier shall be based on the risk assessment (clause 3.5.1.1).

The documented procedures also need to include clear criteria for the ongoing monitoring of existing suppliers. These may include:

- in-house product checks (such as microbiological tests), incoming visual inspections, or checks on the quality of service provided
- provision of certificates of analysis for products
- routine site audit of the supplier
- re-issue of supplier questionnaires.

The company shall maintain a list of approved suppliers and records on which supplier approval is based (e.g. audit reports, completed questionnaires, etc.), complete with any further information on action that was undertaken, in order to demonstrate that supplier approval is adequately controlled.

Procedures should ensure that the site is notified of any significant changes to production processes which may affect the safety, legality or quality of the raw materials.

3.5.1.3   Exceptions procedure

In cases where emergency supplies, commodity purchases or single purchases of a material make it impossible to operate the approval process, the site shall have a procedure detailing how these exceptions are handled. The process will include an assessment of the risk of the purchase and the completion of appropriate checks or tests to mitigate any risk. For example, this may include 100% inspection of the product, certificates of analysis or increased microbiological sampling, according to the risk.

Where products are purchased via agents, information shall be obtained from the agent to ensure that the source of the material is known and that information is made available via the agent or a third party to meet the supplier approval requirements in accordance with the risk assessment.

Where raw materials are obtained from a customer-designated supplier (for example, packaging or when contract packing), the site must ensure that information is obtained about the product and supplier such that potential risks to other products are assessed and controlled.

3.5.2   Raw material and packaging acceptance and monitoring procedures

Controls on the acceptance of raw materials shall ensure that raw materials do not compromise the safety, legality or quality of products.

Verification procedures need to be in place to demonstrate that materials from approved suppliers meet the agreed specifications.

3.5.2.1   Acceptance of raw materials

The acceptance or goods-in system shall include a documented procedure which requires checks to be completed and any non-conformities recorded. The required checks will be based on the previous risk assessment and specification (clauses 3.5.1 and 3.6) and will include one or more of the following:

- visual inspection (e.g. for cleanliness, damaged packaging, infestation)
- temperature checks for chilled and frozen products in particular
- accuracy of product order to ensure the correct materials, grades and quantities have been delivered
- certificates of conformance specific to the consignment
- certificates of analysis specific to the consignment
- specific raw material testing to ensure conformance with specifications before acceptance or use.

The procedure shall also document who is authorised to accept conforming materials and reject non-conforming batches, and the action to be taken.

The acceptance procedures and any testing or sampling requirements would be expected to be available in the goods receipt area and may take the form of a product acceptance matrix identifying materials acceptance criteria and, where applicable, the sampling rate.

3.5.2.2   Implementation of procedures

Records of the raw material checks for each batch of material shall be maintained and are likely to be assessed as part of the BRC traceability audit.

3.5.3   Management of suppliers of services

The company shall be able to demonstrate that where services are outsourced, the service is appropriate and any risks presented to food safety have been evaluated to ensure effective controls are in place.

Supplier approval shall also extend to service provision that affects product safety, legality and quality (for example: the use of agencies to provide temporary staff; or service contracts for laundry, maintenance of equipment (e.g. refrigeration units), waste removal or transport).

3.5.3.1   Approval and monitoring of service providers

The company shall document its procedure for the approval and monitoring of suppliers of services to ensure that these suppliers are capable of providing the service to the required standard.

Approval may include a combination of the following:

- membership of a recognised trade association
- historical experience with the supplier
- legal registration (e.g. waste licences).

It may be appropriate to undertake audits or questionnaires where a service is performed off site and may present a food safety risk (for instance, laundry services for high-care/high-risk clothing). However, this would not be expected of most service providers.

The performance of the supplier should be formally reviewed at a frequency appropriate to the service. For example, an outsourced cleaning service would be assessed as part of the internal audit process (clause 3.4) and records maintained of feedback on performance to the cleaning company. Other services, such as pest control or laundry, may be reviewed with the supplier on a 6-monthly or annual basis and a record kept of the review (e.g. minutes of the meeting).

3.5.3.2 Contracts with service providers

Contracts or formal agreements shall be in place for service providers detailed in clause 3.5.3.1 to ensure the correct level of service is provided.

Service providers who will be on site will need to receive appropriate training to ensure they complete their activities in a way that will not impact on the safety, quality or legality of products being manufactured (clause 7.1.1).

3.5.4 Management of outsourced processing

Where any intermediate process steps in the manufacture of a product which is included within the scope of certification is subcontracted to a third party or undertaken at another company site, this shall be managed to ensure this does not compromise the safety, legality or quality of the product.

This section applies to products included within the scope of a site's certification but which include a process step that is outsourced to another company before the product is returned to the site for further work or packing. Examples of this typically involve a need for specialist equipment (for example, agglomeration of powders, or freeze drying), or alternatively product may be sent to a lower-cost economy for a very labour-intensive part of the process.

Where products are partially processed at one site and finished at another, this is not classed as outsourcing in this context, but the scope of the report and any certificate will reflect only the activities undertaken at the site where the audit was undertaken.

3.5.4.1 Brand owner approval

Customers (e.g. brand owners) must be notified of any intention to outsource part of the production process. (Some brand owners require the opportunity to formally approve or reject this type of outsourcing.) For example, if this is clearly detailed on the approved product specification, then it would demonstrate that the customer has agreed the process.

This requirement is not limited to retail branded products or to certain markets but applies to any product manufactured on behalf of a customer.

3.5.4.2 Outsourced subcontractor approval

Most subcontracted outsourced services will involve working with the product and are likely to have a significant effect upon the quality and/or safety of the products. It follows, therefore, that a high level of confidence is required in the food safety and quality management processes at the service provider. This level of confidence would normally only be achieved by either an in depth supplier audit undertaken by an auditor with audit experience and knowledge of the technology used for the outsourced process or by certification to the BRC Standard or an equivalent GFSI recognised standard (see www.mygfsi.com).

Records of audits and/or reports and certificates for outsourced suppliers need to be maintained and to be available for the BRC audit.

3.5.4.3 Contracts and traceability

Contracts shall be in place for the approved subcontractors detailed in clause 3.5.4.2 to ensure:

- the correct level of service is provided
- the processing requirements are clearly defined in terms of the work to be undertaken, the product/ingredient specification and any relevant quality, safety or legality requirements.

There shall be documented mechanisms to ensure traceability is maintained throughout the process. Records relating to the traceability of individual batches of processed ingredient shall be available.

3.5.4.4   Acceptance and test procedures

A documented acceptance or goods-in system shall identify the checks to be completed when processed material is returned to the site. For example, this may include:

- visual inspection

- chemical, microbiological or allergen testing

- hold/release requirements for the specific raw material (for example, to allow additional testing or QA checks).

The requirements shall be based on risk assessment of the nature of the ingredient, the process and the subcontractor undertaking the processing (for example, the subcontractor may handle allergens that could potentially contaminate the processed product).

The acceptance procedure shall document any non-conformities, who is authorised to accept conforming materials and reject non-conforming batches, and the action to be taken in the event of a non-conformity.

3.6   Specifications

Specifications shall exist for raw materials including packaging, finished products and any product or service which could affect the integrity of the finished product.

The company shall be assured of the quality of the products purchased. This includes any raw material or service that can impact food safety – for example, water and cleaning chemicals used, as well as services such as pest control, cleaning services or distribution.

Specifications for in-house intermediate products (work in progress) shall be developed where they need to be checked and where they have an impact on product safety, legality and quality.

A finished product specification shall exist for all products covered under the certification scope, which ensures that required legislation and customer expectations are achieved.

Current specifications must be available for relevant personnel in order to ensure they are being appropriately fulfilled. This may be the complete specification or parts thereof, or relevant details may be developed as production reference sheets, such as simple photographic specifications.

3.6.1   Raw material and packaging specifications

Specifications for all raw materials, including packaging materials, shall be provided and adequately detailed. They shall include the defined limits for all parameters critical to the safety, legality and quality of the product. They shall also include details of packaging.

The specifications may be in the format provided by the supplier or in the company's own format so long as the information controlling the product's quality and safety are clearly defined.

Specifications for cleaning chemicals shall include components, usage instructions and material safety data.

Specifications for services shall be adequately detailed to allow the company to understand and agree the service parameters they are purchasing and define the level of service required.

3.6.2   Manufacturing instructions and process specifications

It shall be ensured that any manufacturing instructions correctly reflect customer requirements, such as customer specifications, and that the correct recipe is used.

Specifications for work in progress are not applicable for all products but where appropriate (for example, where a product is manufactured in several stages and combined to form the final product or when a product is partially processed and retained for future processing) a specification may be required. It shall detail the important criteria that affect the finished product quality or safety parameters (e.g. brix, weight, colour, shelf life or storage conditions) and shall include the acceptable range of each parameter.

Simple photographic specifications, including minimum, target and maximum grading levels for parameters such as size and colour, may be appropriate for production staff.

3.6.3   Finished product specifications

Specifications shall be in place to control the production of all products.

The format of these should be agreed in advance with the customer.

In the case of the company's branded products, it is acceptable to have an internal specification setting parameters for the manufacture of a product and a technical data sheet for customer use containing the key information for the safe use of the product, including but not limited to:

- ingredients, including the presence of allergens
- nutritional information
- preparation or cooking instructions
- storage instructions
- shelf life/code information
- quantity.

3.6.4   Formal agreement of specifications

Customer branded, finished product specifications shall be formally agreed with the customer and shall, wherever possible, be signed by both parties. However, where the customer's signature or approval is not formally available, proof that specifications have been issued (such as an email request for formal acknowledgement or specifications on customer IT specification systems) is required. In this situation the site must be able to demonstrate it is following a formal process agreed with the customer.

3.6.5   Review of specifications

Specifications shall be reviewed whenever changes occur to the product, process or formulation. Where no changes have occurred, the specifications shall be reviewed at least every 3 years or more frequently if required by a specific customer. Evidence that a review has been completed needs to be available and this should be achieved through the addition of a signature and date to the specification or through the use of a matrix showing specifications and the latest review date and reviewer.

The control of the amendment and approval of specifications should be laid down in a documented procedure. The procedure should also detail who can approve the amendments.

3.7   Corrective action

FUNDAMENTAL

 The company shall be able to demonstrate that they use the information from identified failures in the food safety and quality management system to make necessary corrections and prevent recurrence.

The objective is to ensure there are clear procedures to deal with problems that have the potential to affect safety, legality or quality, ensuring that the finished product and consumer safety are not compromised. This shall include immediate actions and an analysis of the overall issues so that long-term preventive actions may be put in place.

3.7.1   Management of corrective actions

There shall be a documented procedure for handling non-conformities.

All non-conformities generated by the site (e.g. non-conforming product, internal audits, third-party audits or customer complaints) shall be subject to corrective action.

Non-conformities that have the potential to affect product safety, legality or quality shall be recorded, and the responsibility for investigating the cause of problems and ensuring that an adequate response is taken shall be assigned to specified personnel.

Where it is possible that the identified non-conformity may have an effect on other products, then any possible consequences need to be identified and appropriate action taken. In the most extreme situation this could result in the need to recall products.

Corrective actions need to be undertaken as soon as possible to prevent further occurrence of the non-conformity. Immediate actions may need to be undertaken to correct an issue; however, long-term actions may also need to be identified, with appropriate nominated timescales.

All corrective actions undertaken shall be documented. The records will include:

- details of the non-conformity and when it occurred/was identified
- details of the corrective actions (both immediate and any longer-term actions) and dates when the actions were/will be completed
- details of verification checks to ensure corrective action has been implemented and is effective
- details of the root cause analysis and any subsequent actions.

The corrective actions should be included in a regular review of activities and systems. If timescales for actions are not met, it is expected that the reason for this is recorded. The review shall include the effectiveness of corrective action (for example, whether the action has ensured that similar non-conformities will not occur).

ROOT CAUSE ANALYSIS

An important part of an effective corrective action process is the identification of the root cause of the non-conformity and the implementation of suitable preventive action. Root cause analysis is a process of conducting an investigation into an identified problem, to allow the investigator(s) to understand the fundamental cause of the problem and put it right. Whilst there are a number of techniques for undertaking root cause analysis, one of the most common and simplest to use is the 'Five Whys' technique. The technique is based on repeatedly digging deeper into the cause of a problem by asking 'why' to get to the root of the issue. Usually, the root cause becomes evident after five steps, but this number is not fixed and further investigation should be completed where required.

For example: An operator is instructed to perform a simple action, 'weigh out ingredient A'. However, the operator inadvertently uses ingredient B instead. The immediate reaction would probably be that this was an operator error. Whilst this may be accurate, it does not establish the reason why the error occurred or prevent it happening in the future. Using the Five Whys technique, the root cause analysis should ask a series of questions:

- Why did the operator make the error? Conclusion – the operator was unfamiliar with the procedure.

- Why was an operator who was unfamiliar with the procedure asked to complete it? Conclusion – he had been trained but there was no supervision or sign-off of the training to confirm it was satisfactory.

- Why was the training not satisfactory? Conclusion – the two ingredients look identical.

- Why weren't the ingredients clearly labelled? Conclusion – the labels were removed during cleaning and not yet replaced.

- Why weren't the labels replaced? Conclusion – the cleaning staff didn't consider the significance of the delay or the potential for an error.

- Why were the ingredient containers being used if they were not set up correctly for manufacture? Conclusion – checking the labels didn't form part of anyone's duties.

ROOT CAUSE ANALYSIS

- Conclusion of the root cause analysis: what should be changed to prevent recurrence?

  - Update training procedure.

  - Introduce training sign-off procedure to ensure training is understood.

  - Replace labels – if practical, with ones that cannot be removed. Where labels must be removed occasionally, ensure that post-cleaning line checks include a check of signage.

  - Ensure an individual (e.g. the production manager) is authorised and responsible for post-cleaning line sign-off.

  - Ensure cleaning staff fully understand and are trained in the need to return labelling (and all equipment) to a fully operational state.

3.8   Control of non-conforming product

The company shall ensure that any out-of-specification product is effectively managed to prevent release.

The objective is to ensure there are clear documented procedures to deal efficiently with any non-conformance that has the potential to affect product safety or quality. There is also a need to ensure that any non-conforming product or raw material is physically removed from the production process.

3.8.1   Management of non-conforming product

The control of non-conforming product (in this context the implicated product could be any material – for example, an ingredient, final product, packaging or a combination of these) shall be described in a documented procedure which includes:

- Awareness among all staff of the need to report (and to whom) issues which may affect product safety, quality or legality. This may be covered as part of the induction process for production staff.

- The system for labelling and identification of non-conforming product. This may include both direct labelling and computer-based records.

- Segregation/isolation of non-conforming product. Ideally, the product shall be physically segregated by moving it to an identified area within the production site, or clearly marked so that it cannot be confused with in-process material or finished product.

- Where products are manufactured under contract, the brand owner may need to be notified of quality issues and would expect to be contacted where issues affect product safety. Agreement may need to be reached before held product is released for sale. Contacting brand owners is not usually necessary where the decision is to destroy, downgrade or rework product unless this is a contractual requirement of the brand owner.

- Details of staff responsibilities, including which staff have authorisation and responsibility for decisions relating to non-conforming products. The final decision on what to do with product which has been held should be taken by an experienced, technically competent manager. Limited personnel shall have the authority to lift the hold notice or remove product from the isolation area.

- Records shall be maintained of all product placed on hold. These shall include:

  - details of the product quantity and code

  - the reason for isolation

  - action taken/required to assess the suitability of the product

- final decision on what to do with the product
- name of the person authorising the decision and date
- confirmation of the action taken
- any further actions required to prevent recurrence (this may link to an investigation of corrective actions – see clause 3.7)

■ The 'on hold' procedure employed whilst an investigation is completed.

■ Procedures for the effective safe disposal of product.

It is usual to maintain a log of products which are on hold and to undertake periodic physical checks of held stock to ensure that accidental release has not occurred.

The summary of products held and actions taken shall be reviewed as part of the management review process.

3.9 Traceability

FUNDAMENTAL

The company shall be able to trace all raw material product lots (including packaging) from their supplier through all stages of processing and despatch to their customer and vice versa.

As well as being a legislative requirement, traceability is a risk-management tool, allowing food businesses and authorities to withdraw or recall products that have been identified as unsafe. It is designated a fundamental requirement. A traceability system needs to be established at all stages of production, processing and distribution, identifying from whom raw materials have been supplied and to which customers finished product has been supplied. The system shall ensure that products supplied to customers are adequately labelled or identified to facilitate traceability. Traceability details need to be retained in a format that allows access in a timely manner. The Standard expects full traceability one up, one down and through the production process.

3.9.1 Identification of raw materials and finished product

Identification may be achieved by physical labelling of materials/products, by recording systems identifying the allocation of materials to production or mixing areas, or through the use of computerised bar-coding systems. The level of traceability may need to be agreed between the company and its customers, but the system used shall be capable of linking all raw material lot codes through to finished product codes. This will enable finished product to be identified should the recall of a particular batch of raw material need to be instigated.

The limitations of any system must be recognised, as can be demonstrated by the problems associated with bulk storage. Products such as sugar may be delivered with clear batch identification; however, if they are emptied into a single storage tank that is mixed with earlier deliveries, the reduction in accurate traceability is compounded by the potential for product to be trapped in dead zones during filling and emptying. If a particular delivery is identified as being contaminated, this would require disposal of the entire product in the storage tank, and several lot codes of finished product, as the company would not be able to identify the specific batch of finished product that contained the contaminated material.

The traceability system needs to include primary packaging (in direct contact with food), other relevant packaging materials (such as printed outer packaging) and processing aids (substances used within the process but not required to be declared as an ingredient, e.g. sodium alginate for the clarification of beer).

All test results must be traceable to specific batches of product or ingredient.

Consideration needs to be given to how the traceability system operates in practice, e.g. with the effective physical identification of ingredients and products. For example, if bulk containers are labelled, consider how the information is presented to ensure it is legible and accurate. A common non-conformity is the ineffective removal of old labelling details, such as indelible inks or sticky labels, leading to potential errors.

Strict controls on material identification, traceability and segregation are also required to preserve the integrity of any claims made, such as organic status. Where logos are used that make specific claims about production systems (e.g. farm assurance), full traceability shall be demonstrated (see also clause 5.3).

3.9.2   Tests of the traceability system

The traceability system shall be tested at a predetermined frequency and at least annually. This may be completed as part of a real product recall or withdrawal scenario if this has occurred, since the objective is to test the system and identify areas for improvement, rather than supply records of a 'test' for its own sake.

The system shall provide traceability 'forwards' and 'backwards'; therefore, the system should be tested in both directions. For example, a raw material could be selected and traced forward to show in which finished products it was used. A finished product should also be selected and traced back to show all the raw material batch codes that were used to produce it. The tests should include identifying which customers received the finished products and which suppliers provided the raw materials.

The test of traceability should be timed and full traceability would be expected to be achieved within 4 hours. This is to reflect the need for rapid traceability in the event of a recall. Where traceability takes longer than 4 hours, areas where the retrieval of information is slow should be reviewed to identify improvements.

The tests shall also include a quantity check or mass balance. It is not expected that the full mass balance test would always be achievable within 4 hours. The objective is to be able to account for the usage of a full batch of a raw material and this helps to ensure that the traceability systems are capable of operating effectively should a recall be required based on the recall of an ingredient.

The mass balance exercise should usually be undertaken as follows:

- Select a batch code of a particular specific raw material.
- Identify the quantity of raw material supplied under that batch code.
- Identify recipes in which the ingredient is used.
- Use production schedules and batch make-up sheets to calculate the quantities of the selected batch of ingredient used in each product.
- Calculate the quantity of any unused part of the batch in the warehouse (if any).
- Reconcile the quantity delivered against the amounts used plus residual unused stock.

It is acknowledged that quantity checks, in some instances, may take a lot of time and resources to complete successfully.

It is unlikely that the mass balance check will be able to account for all materials to an accuracy of 100%. However, the company needs to justify any discrepancies and demonstrate understanding of the nature of the variance. This may be inherent in the product characteristics – for example, dehydration of fresh ingredients, typical wastage on equipment, or portion variances. The principle is to ensure that the traceability system is effective. Mass balance is a key measure of this workability and highlights areas for improvement.

3.9.3   Rework

Where rework of products or processes is undertaken, consideration needs to be given to how this will affect the product (e.g. that the ingredient declaration on the product is not affected). Procedures shall be in place to ensure that traceability is maintained, and in addition that the safety or legality of products is not affected.

WHAT TO EXPECT AT THE CERTIFICATION AUDIT

During all BRC certification audits, a traceability test and so-called 'vertical audit' will be carried out on a product selected by the auditor which shall have typically been produced in the 2–5 months prior to the audit date. Where a claim is made about a component of the product (clause 5.3), the test shall include a mass balance of the material subject to the claim. The mass balance test should be in both directions (i.e. finished product to raw material and vice versa). It is suggested that the vertical audit (i.e. traceability documentation plus all associated production and raw material documentation) should be carried out only as part of the trace backwards from finished product to raw materials. To undertake such an exercise in both directions would be too time-consuming unless issues are expected. Where the site produces products which make a claim of provenance (clause 5.3), the product selected for the traceability study should be a product for which such a claim is made. Details will be recorded by the auditor and summarised in the final audit report.

This vertical audit is in addition to the review of the company's own traceability checks. The method of achieving traceability will also be reviewed as part of the audit of production areas.

BRC Global Standards publishes a separate *Best Practice Guide to Traceability*, which is available from www.brcbookshop.com.

3.10   Complaint handling

Customer complaints shall be handled effectively and information used to reduce recurring complaint levels.

Complaints are key sources of information that may require escalation into emergency plans such as a product withdrawal or recall. Therefore, an effective complaint handling system needs to be operated by the company. Complaints are also a key measure of product quality and identify opportunities for continual improvement. The objective of the complaint investigation process should be to identify and correct causes of complaints, and one measure of an effective system should be a reducing level of complaints as a proportion of production volume.

3.10.1   Documentation and action

The company should ensure there is a clear process for customers to raise legitimate complaints about the products produced. This is usually via contact information provided on product labels. Where products are supplied into food service or through intermediaries, every effort should be made to ensure that complaints raised by customers are relayed to the complaints department of the site.

A documented complaints procedure is required and the inclusion of a standardised complaint form may be useful. All complaints need to be captured to a central control point to ensure they are adequately assessed and investigated, and the results of this investigation documented.

Complaints shall be handled by appropriately trained staff to ensure that a proactive system identifies the severity, and therefore the significance, of any complaints received.

Actions shall be appropriate to the seriousness of the complaint. A rapid response would be required for serious issues such as a glass complaint, or where a number of complaints are received, suggesting a widespread problem.

A root cause analysis should be carried out where sufficient information is provided in response to serious complaints and emerging trends. A full root cause analysis is not expected for all complaints.

Investigation shall be completed within a defined timeframe and feedback provided to the complainant wherever contact details are provided.

3.10.2   Trend analysis

Data on customer complaints shall be analysed so that trends may be identified. This is to help ensure that the root cause of problems is identified and improvements made to prevent recurrence so far as practicable.

This may include an analysis of foreign-body complaint types as complaint numbers per number of units produced, with data by shift or by production line. This data shall be communicated to relevant staff and may include graphical displays on staff notice boards or discussion at routine operations meetings.

Trend analysis may demonstrate that certain complaints are associated with customer abuse. A root cause analysis of these complaints should be undertaken to establish if the underlying cause can be managed by the company. For example, could on-pack instructions be amended to reduce customer abuse and therefore reduce the number of complaints?

BRC Global Standards publishes a separate *Best Practice Guide to Complaint Handling*, which is available from **www.brcbookshop.com**.

3.11   Management of incidents, product withdrawal and product recall

> The company shall have a plan and system in place to effectively manage incidents and enable the effective withdrawal and recall of products should this be required.

Incidents are events that may result in the production of unsafe, illegal or non-conforming product and risks to consumer safety. An emergency situation may also occur as a result of a sudden, unforeseen crisis that requires immediate action.

An effective emergency plan shall be in place so that if, at any stage, an incident occurs that impacts food safety, legality or quality, it will be managed effectively. The incident may be directly related to the product or may be related to the disruption of key services such as power and water or to environmental influences such as fire or flood.

The plan shall be understood by relevant staff and shall be routinely tested so that it can readily be put into practice, as incidents occur when least expected.

The importance of a tried and tested procedure, ensuring that personnel know who does what and when, cannot be underestimated.

3.11.1   Documented incident and emergency procedures

In the event of an incident or emergency situation, the company shall be ready to instigate actions as promptly and efficiently as possible. The objective of the plan shall be to minimise risk to consumers and potential disruption to business. Systems shall be in place and used to ensure that information is collated and quickly assessed by staff who understand its significance and who can develop an appropriate action plan.

A documented incident management procedure is required. Although it may not be possible to detail exactly what action will be taken, as this will depend on individual circumstances, the company should consider:

- standard responses to a range of potential disasters, such as fire, flood or the loss of essential services
- the provision of alternative resources for energy, water, transport and any potential options for subcontracting production
- how to handle acts of potential malicious contamination or extortion
- details of staff responsibilities, including which staff have authorisation and responsibility for decisions relating to non-conforming products
- methods to communicate with key contacts, both internal and external, such as telephone and email contact details (details shall include office hours and out-of-hours contact details)
- contingency plans and how business continuity is maintained

■ corrective action that needs to be taken before production can recommence.

These details shall be kept up to date by periodic verification.

Customers and suppliers may need to be involved in the development of documented procedures as they may have their own requirements for crisis planning.

3.11.2 Documented withdrawal and recall procedure

The site shall have a documented recall and withdrawal procedure. As a minimum, it shall include:

■ Details of the recall management team members, their roles, responsibilities and contact details. In larger businesses the recall team will involve head-office personnel and may be run from head office. This is clearly acceptable but links between the production-site management and the recall team need to be clear.

■ Guidelines for deciding whether a product needs to be recalled or withdrawn and the records to be maintained. Although causes for recall are often unpredictable, defined responses to known risks (for example, identification of pathogens in routine product sampling) could be documented.

■ An up-to-date list of key contacts – for example, recall management team, suppliers, customers, the Certification Body, regulatory authorities, etc. (Bearing in mind that a recall may be prompted at any time, these details shall include office hours and out-of-hours contact details.)

■ A communication plan including the provision of information to customers, consumers and regulatory authorities in a timely manner. The communication process and the way in which enquiries from customers and the media are handled can be critical to the effective management of the situation and ultimate business recovery, and the use of professional resources to assist in communication management may sometimes be advisable.

■ Details of external agencies providing advice and support as necessary, e.g. specialist laboratories, regulatory authority and legal expertise.

■ A plan to handle the logistics of product traceability, recovery or disposal of affected product and stock reconciliation.

3.11.3 Tests of the withdrawal and recall procedures

It should be emphasised that traceability is only a part of a recall test which is expected to be a test of the effectiveness of the full recall procedures.

The withdrawal and recall procedure shall be tested at least annually. The aims of this are to:

■ demonstrate that the system works

■ highlight any gaps and where the system requires improvement

■ demonstrate how quickly the required information can be collated, and thereby corrective action taken, such as materials being isolated and quarantined

■ act as a training exercise for personnel to ensure that clear roles and responsibilities are undertaken in the event of a real withdrawal situation.

The test of the recall and withdrawal procedure shall include verification of the decision-making process, traceability of raw materials through to finished product, verification of contacts and timings of key activities.

Records shall be kept of tests of the recall and withdrawal procedure and shall include a comment on the result of the test and any action points for improvement.

The results of testing of the product recall and withdrawal procedures shall be reviewed by the senior management to ensure the content and effectiveness of the procedures. If required, the procedures shall be improved.

If the site has had an actual withdrawal or recall which fully tested its recall procedures, then this would substitute for a recall test so long as records are maintained, an analysis of the effectiveness of the recall process is carried out, and any areas for improvement are identified and acted upon.

3.11.4 Notification of recalls to the Certification Body

The principle for informing Certification Bodies is for them to assess whether any change in circumstances affects the certification of the site. There is the potential for the Certification Body to require further information or to carry out a subsequent full or partial audit of the site to confirm certification. The Certification Body shall be informed within three working days of the issue of a recall notification. There is no requirement to notify the Certification Body in the case of a product withdrawal.

Site Standards

4.1 External standards

> The production site shall be of suitable size, location, construction and design to reduce the risk of contamination and facilitate the production of safe and legal finished products.

4.1.1 Local activities and site environment

Local activities and the site environment shall be considered to ensure they do not have an adverse impact on finished product integrity. (A site plan or map that indicates neighbouring activities may be useful.) Points to consider may include:

- derelict buildings, rubbish dumps, wasteland, etc. presenting a harbourage for pests
- adjacent water courses at risk of flooding
- neighbouring companies and the nature of their business, e.g. presenting air or odour taint potential.

Appropriate measures, such as additional pest or flood control, shall be put in place and reviewed to ensure they are continually effective. This may include specific points on regular audit schedules.

4.1.2 Maintenance of external areas

External areas shall be maintained in good order and the condition of the site included in audit procedures.

Overgrown areas can harbour pests; therefore, where areas are planted, they shall be tended regularly. Good practice is to have a 0.5 m clear zone from the bottom of vegetation around external walls, for example.

Drainage in external areas is expected to be able to deal with normal quantities of rainfall without long-term pooling of water. If natural drainage is inadequate, external drainage shall be installed.

To prevent potential contamination by dust or mud, for example, all traffic routes under the control of the company shall be suitably surfaced and maintained in good order. It is recognised that traffic routes may have a variety of surfaces, and contamination risk to products will be influenced by other factors, such as weather conditions. The principle is to ensure that products are not placed at additional risk of contamination through the inappropriate surfacing of routes where products are transferred. Risk may also be reduced by a combination of procedures, such as the suitable protection of products while in transit, or wash-down of transit vessels prior to entering production areas.

4.1.3 Maintenance of the building(s)

The outside of buildings shall be monitored and maintained in a condition such that they do not present a risk of product contamination. For example, pipe work shall be appropriately sealed to prevent pest entry, ingress of water and other contaminants.

4.2 Security

> Security systems shall ensure that products are protected from theft or malicious contamination whilst under the control of the site.

The objective is to ensure that the safety of finished products is not jeopardised through malicious actions or unauthorised persons gaining access to site. Therefore, security systems shall be in place to limit and control access to the external areas of the site, buildings and product.

4.2.1   Documented assessment of security

The company shall undertake an assessment of the security arrangements and risks inherent to the operation. The objective is to prevent unauthorised access to areas where products or ingredients are vulnerable to malicious contamination.

Each area (warehouses, processing areas, external storage areas, etc.) needs to be assessed in terms of how vulnerable the product is to contamination. Open product is likely to be the most vulnerable; the vulnerability of packaged product will depend on the nature of the packaging. Based on the perceived risks, adequate security arrangements shall be identified to reduce the possibility of unauthorised access to products.

These precautions may include:

- site security gates
- the use of CCTV cameras
- keypads or similar systems to restrict access to a building and/or sensitive areas
- controls on the movement of visitors and subcontractors
- locks on external tanks and pipework.

Details of IT systems and data protection should be included within the security assessment.

A report detailing the scope of the assessment, the results and any necessary changes will be documented.

The security assessment will be reviewed periodically (for example, when there is a change to the site or buildings) and at least annually. Records of the review need to be available for the audit.

4.2.2   Authorised access

The basic requirement is that only authorised staff have access to production and storage areas. Restriction of access to areas where sensitive materials are stored (e.g. laboratories, maintenance areas or document storage areas) should also be in place. Where appropriate, areas should be locked when not in use.

To maintain site security, production and storage areas should have designated access points, which should be directly monitored or locked with, for example, keys issued to nominated personnel or key-code locks.

There shall be a visitor reporting procedure. When visitors or contactors come onto site, they should not be able to enter production areas without first reporting to site representatives to be made aware of site rules and to be issued with protective clothing.

All staff shall be trained in the company security procedures and be part of the security arrangements. They should be encouraged to make enquiries or report unknown persons in the facility. This shall not compromise their own personal safety and suspicious activities should always be referred back to security staff where they are available.

All external storage shall be secured.

4.2.3   Registration of food production sites

In countries, states or territories where there is a legal requirement to register premises as food production sites, there shall be documentary proof that the site has been appropriately registered. Examples include the requirement under EC Regulation No 852/2004 on the Hygiene of Foodstuffs, Article 6(2), and registration with the US Treasury under the Public Health Security and Bioterrorism Preparedness and Response Act of 2002.

This clause does not cover other legal registrations related to personnel, health and safety (such as fire regulations) or employment law, as these are outside the scope of the Standard.

4.3   Layout, product flow and segregation

FUNDAMENTAL

> The factory layout, flow of processes and movement of personnel shall be
> sufficient to prevent the risk of product contamination and to comply with
> relevant legislation.

The physical layout and flow of processes, material and personnel shall be identified, designed, managed and
maintained to protect product integrity and prevent contamination.

4.3.1   Designation of product risk zones

Within any manufacturing facility there will be production areas where the product is more or less at risk from
the general environment in which the process takes place. The objective of identifying on the factory plan the
production risk zones is to ensure that the standards of environmental hygiene, particularly those concerning
equipment, buildings, cleaning and personnel hygiene, are appropriate for the work being undertaken. It also
allows product and personnel flows to be reviewed, to ensure they do not compromise product safety.

The Standard has used a classification based on four recognised zones. The concept of 'high-care' and
'high-risk' zones for chilled and ready-to-eat products has been a feature of Issue 4 and Issue 5 of the
Standard, as has 'low-risk' areas. Issue 6 recognises that, in some areas or for some products, the risks are
further reduced where the product is fully enclosed in packaging (warehouse areas) or within pipework or
equipment; these are identified as 'enclosed product areas'.

The Standard includes an appendix which provides a simplistic decision tree and more detailed explanatory
guidelines to help assess the appropriate risk zones for products produced at the site. The guidelines have
been reproduced as an appendix to this document (Appendix 1).

In recent years, there have been well-publicised food-poisoning incidents associated with a wide range of
products which had not previously been considered a concern, e.g. chocolate, peanut butter and cantaloupe
melons. This emphasises that processors need to understand their products thoroughly and configure their
food-safety systems accordingly.

In the BRC Standard Issue 6, particular attention is paid to the groups of products most often associated
with food-poisoning incidents, i.e. chilled or frozen ready-to-eat foods. The Standard defines minimum
hygiene and environmental standards to prevent contamination of these foods after the final process step;
these are classified in the Standard as high-care or high-risk areas. The guidelines for defining products to
be considered for processing in high-care or high-risk areas are based principally on the ability of the food to
support the growth of *Listeria* species.

On this basis, high-care or high-risk zones are applicable for the handling of products which fulfil all of the
following conditions:

- Products are in a form where they are ready to eat or reheat. Therefore, no final microbiological kill step
  is intended to be undertaken by the consumer to make the product safe to eat.

- The final products are stored and distributed chilled or frozen. Although there are a number of ambient
  products which may require special handling, the particular definitions within the meaning of the
  Standard apply to chilled and frozen products.

- The products are vulnerable to the growth of pathogens. In other words, the characteristics or
  formulations of the products – for example, water activity (a_w), absence of preservatives, suitable pH, etc.
  – are suitable to support pathogen growth.

- The products are open and therefore vulnerable to contamination, i.e. they are neither packaged nor
  enclosed within equipment.

It is important to note that the high-care or high-risk production zone usually applies only to part of a factory's production processes: typically following a microbiological kill step and up until the products are enclosed in packaging.

Products have been further divided within the Standard into those requiring high-care environmental processing conditions and those requiring high-risk environmental processing conditions. This is based on whether processing has eliminated *Listeria* through cooking or has reduced the likely incidence through other control measures, such as chlorine washing of vegetables. This ensures that products which have been processed are not placed at risk by other products within the same area that have received only a partial process.

4.3.2   Site plan

In addition to the requirements of clause 4.3.1, the site plan will be expected to illustrate the locations of critical facilities and activities, including:

- access points for personnel
- routes of travel for materials, equipment, people, rework and waste material
- production process flow
- location of staff facilities.

Travel of material or people through processing areas should be managed and restricted to specific routes. These routes must be illustrated and known to staff. The movements of waste and rework must be considered specifically to ensure they do not compromise the safety of products.

4.3.3   Contractors and visitors

Contractors and visitors (including drivers) must be made aware of all access restrictions and procedures related to them. This should occur when visitors sign in and should be specific to the areas they will be visiting.

Contractors that visit regularly should be trained to a similar level as employees and a record of the training retained. Occasional visitors and contractors should be monitored directly.

All visitors shall have someone on site that is responsible for overseeing their work and actions.

4.3.4   Low-risk areas

The HACCP plan shall have identified potential risks associated with production in the low-risk zone and identified the controls (including the level of prerequisite programmes) appropriate for the safe production of the products.

A combination of process flow and procedures (for example, the prerequisite programme and work instructions) will be used to minimise risk to raw materials and products.

It should be recognised that some products classified as produced in a low-risk zone within the Standard's definitions, because they are ambient products, may be capable of supporting the survival of pathogens if re-contaminated following processing. Some of the principles applied to high-care/high-risk areas (for instance, segregated areas and the separation of staff between pre- and post-process areas) may need to be applied. Food-poisoning outbreaks have been attributed to chocolate, peanut butter and dried milk products, all of which can support the survival of pathogens such as *Salmonella* if contaminated.

The procedures developed to ensure product safety in low-risk zones shall be documented, validated as effective and trained to appropriate staff.

4.3.5   High-care areas

This requirement is applicable to high-care areas, i.e. areas designed to a high standard, where practices are in place to minimise product contamination by pathogenic micro-organisms.

Products produced in high-care areas will have undergone a process to reduce any microbiological contamination prior to entering the high-care area, e.g. a chlorine wash of salad materials, or an early cook step (for instance, the use of pasteurised cream). It is important that the high-care area where these products are produced is effectively protected from recontamination from the low-risk zones. This is most effectively achieved through full physical segregation by means of walls which separate the high-care area from other factory areas. Access to the area should be restricted. (The segregation should take into account possible routes of contamination: airborne, personnel, tools, equipment, footwear, etc.).

Where a separate, fully walled-off area is not available, alternative procedures shall be in place to segregate the high-care area and prevent access for unauthorised people, transfer of materials or equipment (except via a controlled route) and microbiological contamination from airborne particles or water droplets. This may include time or space separation, control of movement or other restrictions. The method employed must be validated to demonstrate that the controls are effective in preventing cross-contamination. The auditor will critically examine the arrangements to ensure that potential risks for contamination have been addressed and that the alternative controls are consistently workable before the solution is considered acceptable. (This will be recorded in the audit report.)

Where the solution is time segregation, the changeover between standard and high-care operations should be as infrequent as possible, as it is unlikely that a sufficient standard of cleaning could be reached if changes occur frequently during a day. Fully validated procedures to change the area from low risk to high care are required. These activities need to be taken into account when scheduling production, to ensure effective transformation of the area, including personnel. If the same personnel are responsible for the area during low-risk and high-care operations, they must undergo a complete change of protective clothing.

Where product characteristics meet the description of high care but the systems are fully enclosed (for example, dairies filling cartons with milk), the production area is considered an enclosed production area. However, additional precautions are required when breaking into the lines or filler (for example, for maintenance, to free product jams or for cleaning). Wherever equipment is entered, the necessary hygiene requirements must be completed before packing can recommence.

4.3.6   High-risk areas

High-risk areas require the highest levels of hygiene, working practices, and design and fabrication of facilities and equipment to prevent product contamination with regard to microbiological hazards.

High-risk areas shall be fully separated areas with full physical segregation in place between the high-risk area and other parts of the facility. The purpose of physical segregation is to provide a self-contained area where unprotected high-risk products are handled after the microbiological kill step, until fully protected, usually by means of final packaging. The segregating barrier must be capable of preventing the risk of cross-contamination from movement of staff, equipment or materials, water, other liquids or airborne contaminants. This barrier is expected to comprise a full wall separating the high-risk area from other areas.

Time segregation is not an acceptable alternative for high-risk areas, except for the transfer areas noted below.

The location and operation of all transfer points shall not compromise high-risk and low-risk segregation. For example, this is relevant where raw materials or staff move into a high-risk area. Consideration shall be given to whether this introduces a contamination hazard and may therefore require procedures such as:

- use of disinfection
- removal of outer packaging
- double-door ovens, blast chillers or freezers (i.e. those with a separate entrance and exit)
- controlled air flow (clause 4.4.13).

High-risk areas are expected to be self-contained, fully segregated areas. Best practice is that, where there is a cook step in the production of high-risk products, the cooker becomes the transfer point into the high-risk area via a double-door system, i.e. the cooker is loaded in the low-risk area and unloaded directly into the high-risk area.

Whilst new cooker installations and new-build sites shall incorporate double-door cooking systems, many existing plants are equipped with single-door cookers and have established risk-based procedures for the loading and unloading of the cookers to prevent cross-contamination of cooked products.

The Standard will, therefore, accept the use of single-door cooking systems where a thorough risk assessment has been completed as an interim measure prior to eventual upgrading. Operating practices must be consistently achievable, effective and prevent cross-contamination of cooked products.

The risk assessment must have considered and controlled potential risks from:

- crossover between cooked and raw products in the unloading area

- operators and their clothing, e.g. the handling of cooked products by operators who have previously worked with raw products

- hand contamination resulting from touching surfaces such as common equipment, cooker control panels and cooker door handles

- equipment used for transferring product in and out of cookers

- airborne contamination from low-risk processes, e.g. the loading and unloading area should be separate from the main low-risk processing area

- the floor, e.g. contamination of the wheels of trolleys transferring cooked products to the high-risk area.

When cooked products are unloaded from the cooker they must be moved immediately to a designated high-risk area meeting the requirements of the Standard.

The procedures in operation where single-door cookers are in use will be assessed by the auditor to ensure they are adequate, effective and understood by operators. The audit report shall describe the procedures in place to protect the cooked products from contamination.

High-risk areas contain only components/foods which have undergone a cook or similar process to achieve a 6 log reduction for *Listeria*. Where a single area includes, by necessity, some components which have received a lesser kill, as well as fully cooked components (for instance, in a sandwich preparation area), this will be classed as high care.

4.3.7 Work and storage space

Premises shall be designed to allow sufficient working space and storage capacity so that all operations are carried out properly under safe, hygienic conditions, thereby reducing the potential for cross-contamination between activities due to close proximity. For example, overfull refrigeration storage may lead to doors being left open for extended lengths of time, due to difficulties accessing required materials. This would lead to a non-conformity.

Consideration should be given to all activities in the area, including inspection, cleaning, pest control and maintenance.

4.3.8 Temporary structures

Temporary structures (for example, those constructed during building work or refurbishment) shall be designed and located to avoid pest harbourage, unsanitary conditions and potential contamination of products. For example, where walls have to be knocked through during installation or expansion work, the integrity of the unit shall be preserved to avoid pest entry, and scaffolding used within areas shall be of the appropriate hygienic standard.

Risk assessment of temporary activities or structures should be completed prior to their introduction.

4.4   Building fabric

Raw material handling, preparation, processing, packing and storage areas

The fabrication of the site, buildings and facilities shall be suitable for the intended purpose.

The design, construction and maintenance of the interior of the facility must support effective cleaning and protect products from contamination.

The type of finish to walls, floors and ceilings shall, as a minimum, meet the requirements laid down in any applicable legislation for the industry and be suitable for the intended purpose.

4.4.1   Walls

The walls in areas handling raw materials, preparing, processing, packing or storing product shall be kept in a sound condition and shall be easy to clean and, where necessary, to disinfect. For example, walls shall have a smooth, impervious finish with sealed surfaces, be in a good state of repair and be free from flaking paint.

Tiling of walls should be avoided but, if present, this shall be in good condition, with no cracks or loose tiles.

Ledges should be kept to a minimum or designed with a slope to avoid dust collection. Vulnerable wall surfaces or corners – for example, where vehicles pass in close proximity – should be protected from damage (e.g. with metal plating or barriers properly sealed).

4.4.2   Floors

The floors in areas handling raw materials, preparing, processing, packing or storing product shall be kept in a sound condition and be easy to clean and, where necessary, disinfect. Floors shall be constructed of materials that are impervious, hardwearing, repairable and resistant to chemical attack so that they may withstand appropriate cleaning procedures.

4.4.3   Drainage

Drainage shall be designed and maintained to ensure that product contamination risks are minimised.

Due consideration shall be given to drainage from any internal laboratories or other hazardous operations undertaken on site to ensure that blockages or the presence of micro-organisms could not result in the contamination of process areas.

Drainage systems shall not constitute a potential risk to product (e.g. from potential leakage) when passing through or over production areas. Where feasible, the design of equipment shall ensure that process waste water goes directly to drain to minimise contamination risk. Where significant amounts of water are used (e.g. where wet cleaning is carried out) and direct piping to drain is not possible, floors will have adequate falls to cope with the flow of effluent (i.e. pooling of water should not occur) as this constitutes a splash hazard and, therefore, a contamination risk.

4.4.4   Drainage of high-care and high-risk areas

The flow of drains shall not present a risk of contamination of the high-care/high-risk area.

Drains should flow from high-risk to low-risk areas. There shall be a plan of the drains for these areas which shows the direction of flow and location of any equipment fitted to prevent the back-up of waste water.

4.4.5   Ceilings and overheads

Ceilings and overheads in areas handling raw materials, preparing, processing, packing or storing product shall be appropriately designed and kept in a sound condition to prevent the risk of contamination to product.

Consideration shall be given to prevent the accumulation of dirt, minimise condensation and mould growth, and facilitate cleaning.

In rooms with high ceilings that are difficult to clean or maintain, consideration shall be given to the requirement for line covers over open product to reduce the risk of contamination.

Consideration should be given to mezzanine floors and suspended walkways to ensure they do not present a contamination risk to products below (e.g. they have solid floors/treads).

4.4.6 Suspended ceilings

Where suspended ceilings are used (or roof voids are present), access shall be available for pest control purposes, even if this roof void is not normally used, unless it can be demonstrated that the void is entirely sealed.

Refrigeration equipment is often located in the roof void, and access will be required for maintenance.

4.4.7 Use of windows for ventilation

Where there is a risk to product, such as in production or storage areas, windows and roof glazing that are designed to be opened for ventilation purposes shall be adequately screened to prevent ingress of pests (e.g. by the use of appropriate mesh sizes to cover windows).

4.4.8 Protection of windows against breakage

Where it has been assessed that glass windows pose a risk to product (e.g. where they are in close proximity to production or storage areas), they shall be protected against breakage – for example, by the use of adhesive plastic sheeting.

4.4.9 Doors

Doors shall be in good condition and easy to clean (i.e. they shall provide an adequate level of proofing for the site).

Inspection of doors through which vehicles such as forklift trucks travel is recommended and protection of the door frames with close-fitting metal plates should be considered.

External doors to open product areas such as raw material handling, preparation, processing and packing areas shall not be opened during production, except for emergencies.

Where external doors to enclosed product areas are opened, suitable precautions shall be taken to prevent pest ingress. Strip curtains are a common way of providing this protection. However, these shall be adequately controlled to ensure effective proofing (i.e. they shall not be damaged or missing, they shall reach the floor and they shall be used correctly).

4.4.10 Lighting

Adequate lighting shall be provided to allow:

- staff to be able to monitor quality and defects
- the correct operation of processes
- effective cleaning
- a safe working environment.

Industry guidelines state that preparation, processing and packing areas are generally illuminated to a minimum intensity of 200 lux, with inspection areas requiring higher illumination to 500 lux. All areas need to be considered – for example, poor lighting in storage areas may hinder effective cleaning or inspection.

4.4.11   Protection of lights against breakage

The company shall assess where light bulbs and strip lights pose a risk to product (e.g. where they are in close proximity to production, storage areas or staff facilities) and these shall be protected against breakage. Consideration shall be given to all types of lighting, in order to minimise the likelihood of breakage and the spread of glass shards. This can normally be achieved through the use of shatterproof light tubes, plastic sleeving or diffusion covers. Where full protection cannot be achieved, alternative methods of management, such as wire mesh screens or monitoring procedures, shall be in place.

4.4.12   Ventilation and extraction

Adequate ventilation and extraction shall be provided. Extraction needs to be provided where very dusty operations are carried out or where there is potential for condensation build-up (e.g. in cooking areas or in dry-ingredient handling areas).

4.4.13   Ventilation for high-risk areas

High-risk areas shall be supplied with sufficient changes of filtered air.

A risk assessment shall be completed, the aim being to ensure that air introduced does not contain micro-organisms of concern and will not be the source of additional contamination (for example, through the formation of airborne water droplets). The following should be considered:

- source of air – the air inlet needs to be located to minimise intake of contaminated air (as a minimum, it shall be upwind of potential contaminants such as dust and chemical vapours)
- frequency of air changes
- specification of filter used – there is no absolute standard for the filters; the grade required will depend on the source of the air and the time of exposure of high-risk products/ingredients
- frequency of replacement of filters
- the need to maintain positive pressure compared with adjacent areas, particularly where there is an interface with low-risk areas.

The effectiveness of the system employed should be checked by the use of periodic sampling of air microbiological quality.

Whilst there is no specific requirement for an air over-pressure in high-care areas, good practice is that the ventilation system is in balance, such that there is no large movement of air from low risk into high care.

4.5   Utilities – water, ice, air and other gases

> Utilities used within the production and storage areas shall be monitored to effectively control the risk of product contamination.

The utilities included within this requirement are specifically water, ice, air and other gases that need to be controlled to ensure they do not constitute a contamination risk to product. Other commonly considered utilities, such as electricity, natural gas or fuel, are not included within these requirements.

4.5.1   Water supply

Water used shall be provided in sufficient quantities (e.g. for cleaning operations), pose no contamination risk (e.g. be potable) and conform to relevant legislation by being suitably treated or drawn from mains supply. It may be a requirement for private water supplies and treatment plants to be approved by local or national authorities.

The frequency of analysis of water shall be based on risk, including:

- historical information
- the source of the water (e.g. mains supply or bore hole)

- specific site concerns (e.g. duration of water storage or lead pipes)

- treatments given to the water

- its usage.

It is expected that chemical and microbiological analysis of water shall confirm compliance with national legislation (e.g. EU directive 98/83/EC) or, in the absence of this, with World Health Organization (WHO) standards for potable water. Water quality tests shall be completed at least annually. If the water is supplied by a water authority, a chemical analysis from the authority would suffice for the chemical requirements, unless there are other risks identified in the delivery system (e.g. lead pipes). Where water is extracted from bore holes and/or sites have on-site treatment facilities, additional checks will be required to ensure the water is not contaminated either at bore hole or in treatment.

Consideration shall be given to sampling water at appropriate points of use and this should be documented in a sampling plan.

Where ice is used in products or is in contact with food, this must be produced from potable water and shall be included within the sampling plan.

4.5.2   Water distribution

The aim of this requirement is to identify the key components of the water distribution system. A fully detailed architect's diagram showing complete pipework is not required; a general schematic will be sufficient. The plan enables the site management and auditor to assess potential hazards in the distribution system and ensure that adequate management systems are in place to negate the hazard.

Water holding tanks, for example, may present a microbiological hazard if not covered or if water flow is not controlled to prevent water pooling in areas out of the flow.

Similarly, where water is recycled (for instance, for can cooling), the water needs to be treated and sometimes filtered to ensure a satisfactory water quality is achieved.

Where the source of the water is a bore hole or on-site reservoir, the water treatment processes should be included on the water distribution plan.

The water plan should be taken into account when establishing the best water sampling points to assess the quality of water.

4.5.3   Non-potable water

In most instances the water used in food processing must be potable, as outlined in clause 4.5.1. There are, however, a very few particular situations where non-potable water is permitted for food use – for example, washing of raw fish or livestock. In such circumstances the water used must meet any legislative requirements set for use in this process. The site will also need to have established through the HACCP process that the water used does not present a risk to the final products, e.g. by the introduction of chemical contaminants.

4.5.4   Monitoring of gases and steam

Compressed air, steam or gases used as an ingredient or directly in contact with food shall be monitored to ensure they do not contaminate the product. The main risks to consider are the carryover of boiler water-treatment chemicals in steam, dust particles in compressed air, and oil used as a lubricant in compressed-air systems.

The need for monitoring and the level of monitoring need to be based on an assessment of potential risk. Steam generated from potable water without the addition of additives, for instance, is not likely to present a risk and would not require monitoring.

Compressed air in direct contact with products needs to be filtered prior to use and the filters checked and maintained to ensure these remain effective. The frequency of checks should be documented and based on risk assessment. This should take into account the source of the air, the type of compressors used and the condition of the pipework, e.g. evidence of corrosion. The compressor suppliers or experts should be consulted to establish any potential risk and any necessary testing.

The use of gases, such as those in modified atmosphere packing, shall be demonstrated as being of appropriate quality. Usually, such gases are supplied in a compressed form in metal cylinders and the supplier management process (approved suppliers and specifications, perhaps with certificates of conformance) would be sufficient. In these circumstances, the site would not be expected to undertake its own checks. Compressed gases are generally considered to be microbiologically safe and the Standard does not require routine testing of such gases unless a specific risk has been identified.

There may be additional risks where gases are produced on site and this needs to be evaluated through a risk assessment.

Additional information can be obtained from the British Compressed Air Society (www.bcas.org.uk) and the European Industrial Gases Association (www.eiga.org).

4.6   Equipment

> **All food processing equipment shall be suitable for the intended purpose and shall be used to minimise the risk of contamination of product.**

Suitability includes the condition of the equipment so it does not pose a product contamination hazard, the ability for the equipment to be effectively cleaned and the equipment's ability to achieve the production of safe food products.

Where equipment is stored, storage conditions must ensure that the safety and integrity of the equipment is maintained, so that it cannot become a source of contamination. For example, equipment should be stored clean and in such a way that it does not harbour pests.

4.6.1   Equipment design and construction

Before new equipment is purchased, its intended use should be fully specified so that the equipment can be suitably designed and made of appropriate materials. This shall include consideration of effective cleaning at appropriate frequencies, e.g. design for easy dismantling.

Documented evidence should be available to confirm commissioning prior to use, i.e. trials of operation, cleaning and maintenance.

In order to facilitate routine cleaning, operation, inspection and servicing, equipment shall be appropriately positioned – for example, access provided under, inside and around it. Where it is permanently sited, equipment should be properly secured and may be sealed to the floor to minimise the potential for food debris accumulating beneath where it cannot be cleaned.

4.6.2   Equipment in direct contact with food

This requirement is designed to ensure that equipment is not a source of product contamination, and that it complies with relevant food contact legislation where such legislation exists (for example, in the EU, the Materials and Articles in Contact with Food Regulation 2004/1935 and its subsequent amendments). In general, sites should use approved suppliers that are known to supply products designed for food use. New equipment should be purchased with a certificate of conformity or specification demonstrating that food-contact surfaces are suitable for food use. This may also be confirmed by labelling (e.g. in the EU, the 'wineglass and fork' symbols).

Food-contact surfaces manufactured from suitable grades of stainless steel are used extensively in the food industry.

Issues have arisen through the purchasing of equipment (especially plastic items) not designed for food use – for example, plastic refuse bins for ingredient storage. This can lead to the migration of chemicals into food products.

Where evidence to confirm the suitability of food-contact equipment is not available, and the contact material is not a recognised food-safe material (such as stainless steel), a documented risk assessment should be carried out to justify its use and ensure that it is not a food safety risk. The risk assessment shall consider factors such as:

■ the nature of the food-contact surface and its known characteristics

■ the length of contact time with the food

■ the nature of the food and its potential for contamination (e.g. fatty foods are often at risk from migration of contaminants from plastic materials).

The assessment shall also consider the cleaning methods and chemicals used and their effects on the material's integrity. Further clarification should be sought (e.g. from the equipment manufacturer or cleaning-chemical supplier, or from testing such as migration tests) where required.

4.7   Maintenance

An effective maintenance programme shall be in operation for plant and equipment to prevent contamination and reduce the potential for breakdowns.

To ensure that all equipment (including fixtures and fittings) is suitably maintained and does not pose a product contamination risk, it shall be controlled by a documented maintenance system. Planned maintenance may be completed internally or via contracted services. Maintenance undertaken internally shall be documented in the form of a plan and records shall be maintained. For equipment that is maintained under external contracts, evidence of contractual agreements shall be available.

4.7.1   Documented maintenance schedule

There shall be a documented planned maintenance schedule or condition monitoring system in place for all items of plant and processing equipment relevant to the production of food.

When commissioning new equipment and plant, a documented maintenance programme shall be established, based on risk assessment and information supplied by the equipment manufacturer or supplier (for example, planned preventive maintenance, recommended maintenance checks and frequencies).

4.7.2   Equipment inspection

Where there is a risk of foreign bodies contaminating product due to wear or damage to equipment or pieces of machinery (e.g. sieves, mills, equipment covers, etc.), there shall be a periodic check of the equipment. This may be achieved by a documented check procedure carried out at defined intervals – for example, at process start-up, following breaks, and after cleaning or maintenance.

Inspection results shall be documented and, where appropriate, action taken.

4.7.3   Temporary repairs

Temporary repairs shall be kept to a minimum and used only in an emergency. They must be controlled to ensure that the safety or legality of product is not jeopardised and a system shall be in place to demonstrate that a permanent repair is planned within a defined timescale (e.g. a works order).

4.7.4   Post-maintenance cleaning

The site shall ensure that the safety and legality of product is not jeopardised during maintenance and cleaning operations (e.g. equipment is not contaminated either by products used during the maintenance, such as sealants, nuts and bolts, or by machinery parts that have broken or disintegrated and have not been adequately removed).

Wherever practical, maintenance work should be undertaken outside of production hours.

A procedure shall be in place to ensure that, following maintenance work, equipment is cleaned and all engineering equipment and debris removed before the equipment is returned to production. Records need to be maintained to demonstrate that the equipment has been inspected and is acceptable for use.

Best practice is for an authorised member of staff (e.g. the production manager) to formally accept equipment back into operation following an inspection, to confirm that maintenance and associated cleaning have been completed satisfactorily. A record shall be completed – for example, by signing the appropriate engineering record.

4.7.5   Use of food-grade materials

Materials used for equipment and plant maintenance that pose a risk of direct or indirect contact with raw material, intermediates or final product shall be of food grade. Documentary evidence of the food-grade status shall be held – for instance, in a declaration by the supplier or on product data sheets.

4.7.6   Engineering workshops

The engineer's workshop shall be controlled to minimise potential for contamination of product.

Consideration should be given to location and design, as well as procedures for control. For example, where it is not possible to avoid having an entrance directly from engineering to the production area, procedures such as use of 'swarf' mats shall be in place to prevent contamination risks (e.g. debris being carried inadvertently into the production area). Workshops need to be kept clean and tidy, and operated in a controlled manner.

Consideration should also be given to the provision and location of hand-washing facilities for engineers entering the factory.

4.8   Staff facilities

Staff facilities shall be sufficient to accommodate the required number of personnel, and shall be designed and operated to minimise the risk of product contamination. The facilities shall be maintained in good and clean condition.

This clause focuses on staff facilities from the perspective of eliminating product contamination.

Appropriate staff facilities shall be provided to enable staff to adhere to company policies (for example, the correct storage of protective clothing and personal belongings), to ensure the risk of product contamination is kept to a minimum. This shall include adequate facilities to accommodate staff fluctuations, such as high production times and the use of agency staff.

Washing, changing and toilet facilities provided for visitors and contractors shall be of a standard that allows non-staff members to meet suitable levels of hygiene. Best practice is that visitors and contractors follow exactly the same changing routine as staff (e.g. change in changing areas and not in management offices).

4.8.1   Changing facilities

Designated changing facilities shall be provided for all staff (including visitors and contractors). The location and position of facilities is an important consideration and this shall be the subject of a risk assessment to ensure the protection of protective clothing from contamination before entering the production areas.

The size of the facilities needs to be adequate for the number of staff working at the factory and consideration must be given to ensuring that facilities are adequate at times of peak staff numbers.

Where it is not possible to locate changing facilities with direct access to the production, packing or storage areas without recourse to any external area, a risk assessment shall identify where additional procedures need to be implemented (e.g. providing cleaning facilities for footwear where footwear is worn outside, or the donning of additional protective clothing on entry to production areas).

4.8.2   Storage of personal items

To prevent staff from bringing personal items into production and storage areas, where they could become foreign bodies, there shall be sufficient and suitably secure storage for employees' belongings. Consideration should be given to the storage of bulky items such as motorbike leathers and helmets, as well as items such as jewellery and food.

4.8.3   Segregation of personal items from workwear

Separate storage facilities for personal items and work clothing are necessary to prevent cross-contamination of clothing via the locker.

This is often achieved by using a locker with divider to separate workwear from personal clothing, but it may also be achieved by enclosing protective clothing in a bag, such as the laundry bag, before use.

Due to the potential for cross-contamination, clean protective clothing shall be segregated from dirty protective clothing (e.g. through the provision of separate locker areas).

4.8.4   High-care changing facilities

The objective of this clause is to ensure that protective clothing, once applied, is not contaminated before entry into the high-care area.

Normally these changing facilities are physically segregated from other changing areas. However, in exceptional circumstances it may be possible for a site to use time segregation, i.e. changing facilities shared with low-risk staff but with different shift patterns to ensure that low-risk staff do not use the facility at the same time. It may be necessary for changing facilities to be cleaned between different groups of workers, depending on the risk. The auditor must be satisfied that the potential risks have been assessed and that the procedures are capable of being operated consistently without abuse.

Documented instructions shall be available, advising staff to:

- apply dedicated personal protective clothing which is visually distinct (e.g. different in colour or style), including clean overalls, headwear and dedicated footwear (by exception, shoe coverings can be provided for visitors but these are only to be worn in the high-care area)
- apply clothing in a given order (e.g. hairnet first, then shoes, then overall)
- wash hands during the changing procedure.

There shall be an effective system to differentiate areas for wearing high-care footwear (e.g. a barrier or bench system) or there shall be an effective boot wash on entrance to the high-care area.

High-care protective clothing shall not be worn outside the designated high-care area.

On entry to high-care areas, all staff, visitors and contractors shall wash and disinfect hands.

4.8.5   High-risk changing facilities

For facilities manufacturing high-risk products, personnel shall enter the high-risk area via a specific designated changing facility (i.e. separate from other, lower-risk changing areas) and shall follow documented instructions to:

- apply specific dedicated protective clothing which is visually distinct (e.g. different in colour or style), including clean overalls, headwear and footwear
- apply clothing in a given order (e.g. hairnet first, then shoes, wash hands, then put on protective overall)
- wash hands during the changing procedure.

Footwear to be worn in high-risk areas must be dedicated to the factory, i.e. factory issued and not worn outside the factory. It is expected that the footwear is also captive to the area, i.e. worn only in the high-risk area. The changing area must be laid out with an effective system to differentiate areas for wearing high-risk footwear (e.g. by the use of a barrier or bench system).

By exception, boot-wash facilities may be used instead of changing into captive footwear dedicated to the high-risk area.

The use of boot-wash facilities at the entrance to a high-risk area will be acceptable where this is managed and validated to effectively prevent the introduction of pathogens. The site shall have undertaken a risk assessment to identify the suitability of the boot-wash facilities and controls to manage the effective sanitation of footwear. The controls shall have been validated by microbiological swabbing of footwear and the floors and drains in the high-risk area, to demonstrate the absence of *Listeria* species.

For such controls to be effective, they would be expected to include the following:

- The footwear shall be company issued and of a design which is easily cleaned, i.e. smooth upper surfaces, and cleats on soles shall be sufficiently spaced so as not to trap dirt which may not be easily removed by boot-wash equipment.

- The potential for cross-contamination of boots prior to boot washing shall be considered, i.e. the footwear shall not be worn outside of the facility or in low-risk processing areas prior to entering the high-risk area.

- The boot-wash equipment shall be suitably designed, well maintained and demonstrably effective in cleaning and sanitising the footwear.

- The minimum cleaning time and levels of detergent and sanitiser used shall be determined, documented and controlled to ensure effective cleaning of footwear.

Records shall be maintained of detergent/sanitiser checks, and of the effectiveness of the boot-wash facilities.

All visitors and contractors entering the area will need dedicated footwear; shoe covers are not satisfactory for high-risk areas.

High-risk protective clothing shall not be worn outside the designated high-risk area.

The objective of the use of dedicated high-risk clothing is to prevent the potential contamination of products. If the cleaning team (or indeed anyone else, such as engineers/visitors) enter a high-risk area whilst production is in progress or open products are present, they must follow the same clothing rules as production staff. If cleaning occurs outside of production time, the absolute rules on protective clothing may be adapted but must ensure that the production area is left in a condition, after cleaning, such that no microbiological risks have been introduced by the cleaners or equipment used. The same principles apply to engineers undertaking maintenance work (which should be followed by cleaning to restore the microbiological security of the area).

On entry to high-risk areas, all staff, visitors and contractors shall wash and disinfect their hands.

It is generally expected that, wherever practical, auditors will observe the cleaning in high-risk areas, to ensure that the practices used are effective and that controls are in place to prevent this activity introducing new risks.

4.8.6   Hand-washing facilities

Dedicated hand-washing facilities shall be provided at entrances to production areas and, where appropriate, at additional points within production areas. This is to ensure that hands are physically washed, rather than just sanitised, before starting work and as necessary during the working day. In some low-risk operations, the hand wash prior to entry to production may be in a changing facility or toilet rather than within the entrance to the actual production area. In some dry environments where water is to be avoided, gel or alcohol sanitisers may be used in the production areas in place of hand-washing facilities, although staff will still be required to wash their hands before entering the production area.

The hand-washing facilities shall be equipped with:

- water in sufficient quantities and at a suitable temperature (comfortably warm is about 45°C (113°F))

- soap solution

- suitable hygienic hand-drying facilities (either single-use hand towels or suitably designed and located hand driers; roller towels are not acceptable as they are not single use)

- appropriate instructions for use, considering the language needs of staff (e.g. including pictorial instructions)
- taps that have hands-free operation.

Best practice is that hand sanitiser is also provided at all hand-washing facilities. (Hand sanitiser is always required for high-risk and high-care operations.)

The provision and location of hand-wash basins will be expected to follow industry best practice within that sector. For some low-risk operations, where hand-washing facilities are not available at each entrance, and are provided within toilets as the only means before re-entering production, these requirements will apply to toilet areas.

4.8.7   Toilets

Toilets shall be adequately segregated from production areas and shall not open directly into production. It is expected that there is an intermediate ventilated space between the toilet cubicle and any production area to prevent foul odours from entering production areas.

The hand-washing facilities provided in toilets shall be equipped with:

- sufficient water at a suitable temperature
- soap (in any format)
- suitable hand-drying facilities (in any format)
- appropriate instructions for use, considering the language needs of staff.

Where hand-washing facilities within toilet facilities are the only ones provided before re-entering production, the requirements of clause 4.8.6 shall apply, including suitable signage to direct staff to wash their hands prior to entering production.

4.8.8   Smoking areas

Facilities in line with national legislation shall be provided for those staff wishing to smoke. These facilities shall not be located within the packing or production areas, where there is open food or ingredients, or where smoke could reach product or ingredients. Indoor facilities shall have sufficient extraction to the exterior of the building.

Suitable facilities for staff to remove their protective clothing before smoking and for washing their hands afterwards shall be provided. Signs shall direct them to hand-washing facilities.

There shall be sufficient and appropriately positioned facilities for the waste generated by those persons smoking.

4.8.9   Staff food

Suitable storage facilities shall be provided for food brought onto the site by staff, enabling it to be stored in a hygienic manner. In countries, states or territories where fridges in the home are the norm, they would be expected to be provided in the workplace, kept clean, maintained and operated at an appropriate temperature. Fridges used for production materials and shelf-life samples shall not be used for storing staff foodstuffs.

No food (including sweets and chewing gum) shall be taken into storage, processing or production areas, as it may constitute a risk to the product. Food shall be adequately controlled when stored in other areas.

All food and drink shall be consumed in designated areas away from food handling, production and storage areas. Where appropriate, designated outside areas can be provided for staff to eat food. Where provided, these shall have appropriate control of waste.

Drinking of water from purpose-made dispensers and/or by using disposable conical cups or spill-proof containers may be allowed, provided it is confined to a designated area, minimising the risk to product, and suitable disposal facilities are provided.

4.8.10   Catering facilities

Where the company provides a canteen or other food service (including food vending services) for members of staff, the kitchens and cold-storage areas need to be suitably controlled to provide safe food and prevent the contamination of products (for example, by microbiological or allergen contamination).

It would be expected that, where catering facilities are provided, a study based on HACCP principles will have been carried out and the risks identified will be effectively controlled. In particular, staff hygiene standards, cleaning, cross-contamination between raw and cooked foods, and storage conditions should be managed effectively. At the audit there will be a basic inspection of the kitchen facilities. Catering facilities should be part of the site's own internal audit or hygiene inspection programme.

In some operations (for example, sites manufacturing a product with an allergen claim), specific allergens present a particular risk and these sites should specify company policies to confectionery vending suppliers and catering facilities. An example is the requirement for no nut products on a site where a company is manufacturing 'nut-free' products.

4.9   Chemical and physical product contamination control

Raw material handling, preparation, processing, packing and storage areas

Appropriate facilities and procedures shall be in place to control the risk of chemical or physical contamination of product.

The risk of foreign-body and chemical contamination shall be minimised through the consideration of potential sources and the implementation of control procedures. This shall have been considered within the HACCP food safety plan.

Areas to consider include storage, processing, equipment, maintenance, building structures, cleaning operations and personnel. Staff facilities and communal areas such as entrance corridors also need to be considered to ensure that their design and the processes carried out within them do not pose a risk to products (e.g. the presence of staples or drawing pins in open notice boards). Regular site inspections (clause 3.4.4) shall be carried out to verify that these controls are in place.

4.9.1   Chemical control

4.9.1.1   Non-food chemicals

Non-food chemicals present a potential product contamination hazard or taint risk if they are not stored and handled correctly. The site needs to demonstrate controls on non-food chemicals, including the following:

- An approved list of chemicals for purchase – this is to ensure that there is a considered process that prevents inappropriate chemicals being purchased. This applies to all cleaning chemicals, pesticides and other chemicals which may be used in the production environment.

- Material safety data sheets and specifications provided by the supplier.

- Confirmation that the chemicals are suitable for use in a food-processing area, i.e. they are non-tainting and not highly toxic.

- Avoidance of strong-scented products.

- Identification of chemicals (e.g. labelling of all containers) at all times, to minimise the potential for inadvertent use.

- Segregation and secure storage, with access by authorised personnel. Potentially harmful chemicals (e.g. sodium hypochlorite) shall be secure and access shall be restricted. Good practice is to provide bunded areas around appropriate chemical and oil tanks and ensure that safe-use/storage instructions from the manufacturer are implemented (for example, store acid and alkaline materials away from each other and store powders above liquids in case of spillage and subsequent reaction).

■   Use of chemicals by trained personnel only, as evidenced by training records.

Chemicals that are likely to come into direct contact with foods when used as intended (for example, materials such as oils or lubricants used on machinery), as well as terminal sanitisers that are designed to be used without rinsing with water, should be confirmed as suitable for food use. (This would not include general detergents and cleaning materials, as these should not come into direct contact with food.)

Consideration may need to be given to the legislative requirements of specific countries, states or territories. For example, legislation may require that materials do not contain toxic or prohibited substances, that lubricants are suitable for food use or that terminal sanitisers meet applicable standards (in the EU, the Biocidal Products Directive 98/8/EEC).

4.9.1.2   Strong scents and taints

Wherever possible, strongly scented or taint-forming materials shall not be used. However, where these are necessary (e.g. for some building work), procedures shall be in place to prevent the risk of taint contamination of products. For example, relevant information shall be requested from contractors, detailing the chemicals to be used and the controls (such as the extraction of fumes) that will be in place. A risk assessment of the information should be completed prior to commencement of the work.

4.9.2   Metal control

4.9.2.1   Sharp metal implements

Where sharp metals such as knives, needles or cheese wires are used, there shall be a documented policy. This will outline:

■   the controls in place

■   inspection and breakage/loss reporting procedures

■   other controls, such as issue and return logs.

The company should aim to ensure that shards of missing metal are located and that the source of any loose metal is identified.

Snap-off blades, i.e. where the old segment of blade can be snapped off to reveal a new sharp edge, are a source of potential metal contamination and are not permitted in any area of production or storage.

Other metal items, such as non-production blades, engineering tools and equipment, shall be stored away from production areas to minimise their potential for contaminating product. For example, spanners used for adjusting machinery should not be left out, but should have a designated place for storage, such as a locked toolbox fixed to a wall.

4.9.2.2   Staples, paper clips and similar metallic items

Staples are often used in packaging. However, their use needs to be considered, since they are a potential source of contamination and the purchase of ingredients or packaging materials containing them shall be avoided. Where ingredients with potential foreign bodies cannot be avoided, there need to be controls to manage these hazards.

Staples and paper clips shall not be used in open product areas.

4.9.3   Glass, brittle plastic, ceramics and similar materials

4.9.3.1   Exclusion of unnecessary materials

The company shall undertake an assessment of glass and other brittle items in open product areas and areas where there is a risk of contamination of product or packaging and, wherever possible, remove these items. Where it is not possible to remove all items, they shall be protected against breakage (e.g. by the use of adhesive plastic sheeting, reinforcement or shielding) and included on a register for inspection purposes (clause 4.9.3.2). This clearly does not apply to glass or brittle materials used to pack final products, which are covered separately in clause 4.9.3.4.

4.9.3.2   Documented handling procedures

Procedures for handling glass and similar materials need to be documented to ensure that the risks of product contamination are managed.

The documentation shall include:

- A list or register of items, detailing their location, number, type and condition. When creating the list, it is important to be realistic; the objective is to remove brittle items where possible and create a list of items for inspection which present a real risk of breakage and contamination of products. (The list could also detail the frequency with which the items shall be checked.)

- Recorded, routine inspections to verify the condition of these items. Inspections shall be carried out at a specified frequency based on risk assessment; some areas may be checked more frequently than others due to their potential to form a foreign-body hazard in the product. (For example, a factory identifies part of the production line which has plastic laminated line covers that may chip or break. The condition of this section of the line is specifically checked on a daily basis prior to production, because it is above open food and any break or damage is likely to result in a foreign-body issue. The same factory has a brittle plastic dial cover on a control panel on the exterior of a piece of equipment not close to open product. This is checked only monthly, as a break and subsequent foreign-body issue is unlikely.) A record of the inspection shall be maintained even when there is no change in the condition of the inspected items.

- The systems that allow cleaning or replacement in such a manner as to minimise potential risk to products (e.g. replacing bulbs in fly-killing devices).

4.9.3.3   Breakage procedures

There shall be documented procedures detailing the course of action to be taken when a breakage of a glass, brittle or hard plastic material, ceramic or similar item occurs. This shall be based on risk assessment (therefore, the action taken may depend on the area in which the breakage occurred) and should include:

- isolation and inspection of potentially contaminated product (raw materials, packaging, final product, etc.)

- isolation of potentially contaminated area (e.g. specifying a 10 m exclusion zone)

- how to clear up the broken item

- how to clean the area and which cleaning equipment to use – this is important to ensure that glass particles are not transferred on equipment from one area to another

- how to dispose of debris

- inspection of the production area after cleaning, and the authorisation to recommence production

- changing of production workwear (staff and cleaners)

- inspection of footwear (staff and cleaners)

- who to inform

- records to keep

- management of implicated product (e.g. product disposal)

- identification of authorised staff to complete the above actions.

4.9.3.4   Products packed into glass or other brittle containers

Where products are packed into glass or other brittle materials (for example, ceramic pots), the risk of breakage is increased and the packaging materials themselves present a significant foreign-body risk. This section deals specifically with the additional controls required to reduce the risk of contamination. This section is not applicable where products are not packed into glass or similar brittle containers.

4.9.3.4.1   Storage

There shall be dedicated, segregated storage for containers.

So far as is practical, a separate storage room shall be used for storage of empty containers. Where the containers are in a shared warehouse, a distinctly separate area must be used. Consideration must be given to warehouse product flow to reduce the risk of broken glass or fragments being carried into raw-material storage areas.

4.9.3.4.2 Breakages

In addition to the points identified in clause 4.9.3.3, procedures shall be in place to manage container breakages between the container cleaning/inspection point and container closure. These shall include documented instructions for:

- The identification, removal and disposal of at-risk products in the vicinity of the breakage. (Separate instructions may be required for different equipment or areas of the production line. Where this is appropriate, the instructions will clearly indicate the section or equipment to which they apply.)

- The effective cleaning of the line or equipment. Consideration is needed to ensure that the cleaning procedures do not result in the further dispersal of fragments (for example, through the use of high-pressure water or air).

- The use of dedicated, clearly identifiable (e.g. colour-coded) cleaning equipment. Such equipment shall be stored separately from other cleaning equipment.

- The use of dedicated, accessible lidded waste containers for the collection of damaged containers and fragments.

- The inspection of production equipment following the cleaning, to ensure that any risk of further contamination has been removed.

- The authorisation for production to restart following cleaning and inspection.

- Ensuring the area around the line is kept clear of broken glass.

Where high-speed filling lines are used with automatic breakage detection and cleaning systems, the above practices will not all be practical. Where such automatic systems are in use, the site must be able to demonstrate that the system is capable of consistently and safely removing glass fragments and that factors which may affect the performance of the clean and/or rejection of implicated products (e.g. low water pressure) are understood, documented and controlled.

4.9.3.4.3 Records

All breakages shall be recorded. This record should include:

- the location where the breakage occurred

- a record of the action taken

- sign-off by an authorised member of staff.

Where no breakages have occurred during a production period, this shall also be recorded.

The record shall be reviewed to identify trends – for example, during the management review of incidents (clause 1.1.3).

4.9.4   Wood

The use of wood is not permitted in production areas except where it is a requirement of the process (for example, wooden casks used for some alcoholic beverages).

Wooden pallets should not be present in open product areas.

Where wood cannot be avoided, a procedure shall be in place to:

- identify damaged items

- minimise the potential for contamination

- include regular checks to ensure wood is in good condition and clean.

4.10   Foreign-body detection and removal equipment

The risk of product contamination shall be reduced or eliminated by the effective use of equipment to remove or detect foreign bodies.

The risk of foreign-body contamination shall be minimised using food industry best practice, such as X-ray inspection, metal detection, sieves, magnets or scanner technology.

BRC Global Standards publishes a separate *Best Practice Guideline on Foreign Body Detection*, which is available from www.brcbookshop.com.

4.10.1   Foreign-body detection and removal equipment

4.10.1.1   Documented assessment

The HACCP analysis should be the starting point for implementing an effective foreign-body control programme. Potential hazards, and the sources of those hazards, shall be identified so that appropriate control procedures can be put in place to minimise the likelihood of product contamination.

4.10.1.2   Type, location and sensitivity

The choice of location for foreign-body detection equipment is vital for its effective use. Equipment should be placed as close to the end of the production process as is practical, so that the whole process (including packing lines) is protected.

Consideration should be given to potential environmental effects (for example, temperature, moisture or speed of line) and these should be discussed with the equipment supplier when selecting equipment and determining the best location.

The sensitivity of detectors shall be specified and best practice applied, taking into account the nature of the food, contamination characteristics, and the location and aperture size of the detector, all of which influence sensitivity. For example, it is likely that metal detectors will have sensitivity to ferrous, non-ferrous and stainless steel test pieces, with sizes used according to industry best practice for the particular product type.

The standard expects validation of the detector and its location. Validation should be undertaken at set-up – for example, by adjusting the machine sensitivity using a range of typical products to establish the most sensitive practical setting which allows consistent rejection without false rejects. The established settings shall be recorded and verified through regular checks of the equipment, generally undertaken using test pieces of a size just above the limit of detection.

4.10.1.3   System tests

The test frequency must be defined in procedures.

The frequency of routine tests should consider:

- the need for additional checks at start-up and finish of shifts
- product changeovers
- the need for regular checks throughout production (hourly testing is expected for many detection systems)
- changes in machine settings or following downtime
- any specific customer requirements
- the site's ability to recover and retest product in the event of a failure.

In the event that equipment is discovered not to be working, all of the product that has passed through the detector since it was last verified to be working should be rechecked.

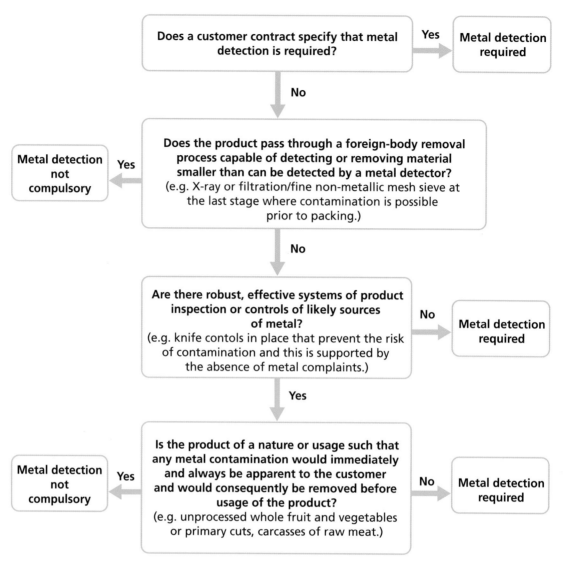

Where the product is packed into metal packaging, an effective alternative test method must be developed – for example, X-ray or metal detecting the product at the stage prior to packing, or the use of magnets and product inspection.

Figure 1 Decision tree for metal detection

4.10.1.4   Investigation of rejected material

Products rejected by detection systems can provide valuable information about possible problems arising from raw materials or the production process, and provide an early warning of potential issues. Rejected products should, therefore, be examined to identify the cause of rejection. Identified causes should be investigated and recorded.

The data on rejected product shall also be used as the basis for analysing trends. This trend analysis may be used to establish preventive actions to reduce future contamination. Information about false rejects should also be recorded, because this may suggest an error with the detector or indicate that the settings are too sensitive for a particular product and require adjustment.

4.10.2   Filters and sieves

4.10.2.1   Mesh and gauge size

To ensure the system provides maximum protection, consideration shall be given to mesh and gauge size. The smallest practical size should be used.

The size will be documented and details easily available to staff using the equipment.

Material retained or removed by the system shall be examined and recorded to identify contamination risks. This information should be reviewed and, where appropriate, remedial action taken. For example, the sieving of bulk flour might identify an issue with infestation in the flour handling system. This could be discussed with the pest control company and potentially the raw material supplier to ensure correct controls are in place. Remedial action shall be documented.

4.10.2.2   Routine inspection

Filters and sieves shall be monitored to ensure they themselves do not pose a foreign-body hazard and are working effectively. There shall be a documented procedure which includes the frequency of checks, responsibilities and action to be taken when issues are identified. The frequency of checks should be based on the nature of the sieve (e.g. a perforated-drum sieve is less likely to fail than a wire-mesh sieve), historical evidence of performance and risk to finished product. It would be difficult to justify an inspection frequency of less than once per week. The results of sieve monitoring shall be recorded.

Consideration should be given to the material from which sieves and filters are manufactured, to minimise the potential for breakages leading to potential foreign-body issues. Where sieves or filters are used as part of a justification for not requiring metal detection, they shall be made of non-metallic mesh.

Where defective filters or sieves are identified, this shall be recorded, the potential for contamination of products investigated and appropriate action taken.

4.10.3   Metal detectors and X-ray equipment

4.10.3.1   Requirement for metal detection

The Standard makes a general presumption that metal detection provides improved protection for customers and should form part of the food protection system of a site. There will, however, be situations where metal detection does not, on the basis of risk assessment, provide any significant additional protection of the consumer.

Where metal detectors are not used, a risk assessment must be available to justify the reasons why they are not required. Whilst complaint levels are a factor in making a decision on the necessity for metal detection, this evidence alone will not be sufficient justification that a metal detector is not required. (For example, there may be instances of contamination which have not been reported by consumers.) Any justification for the absence of metal detection should be based on the nature of the product, the risk to the consumer and alternative controls in place at the site which prevent metal contamination. The absence of metal detection cannot be justified on the basis of cost alone.

In all circumstances where products are manufactured to a customer's specification, sites must comply with any customer requirement for metal detection of their products.

The decision tree in Figure 1 provides further guidance on the need for metal detection equipment for products not packed into metallic containers.

4.10.3.2   Location of metal detectors or X-ray equipment

Detection equipment shall be located to maximise its effectiveness. Generally, best practice is to have it positioned following primary packaging of product (the obvious exception to this rule is where the product uses metallic packaging, which would prevent foreign-body detection) or at a point where there is no further risk of foreign-body contamination.

4.10.3.3   Rejection mechanisms

Issue 6 of the Standard requires the use of automatic rejection devices to be incorporated with metal detection and X-ray equipment. The objective is to ensure that rejected products are not accidentally reintroduced into the process flow. The use of stop-belt and alarm systems may present a greater risk of accidental reintroduction of rejected products unless this is well controlled.

Following consultation, it has been accepted that stop-belt-style metal detector rejection systems will continue to be acceptable for all pack types where additional controls are in place to ensure the effective removal and isolation of products identified as potentially containing metal. Typically this will include the use of a container into which rejected product is placed, which is secured such that only authorised staff can remove the product (similar to the locked-box system used for automatic rejection systems).

The following additional controls should be considered to ensure that rejected product is effectively segregated and managed:

- The removal of affected product should be restricted to trained, authorised staff. This may be supported by restricting access to the product once the belt has stopped, e.g. by using locked line cover and authorised key holders.

- Rejected product may be marked, destroyed or have its label removed to reduce the risk of reintroduction to the process flow.

- The line restart should be restricted to designated personnel who must verify the location of the 'rejected' product prior to restart (i.e. the control panel/button for restart is secure, locked or security coded).

- A record should be made of each occasion when the belt stops in response to the detection of metal in a product.

4.10.3.4   Documented metal detector and X-ray procedures

The site shall have documented procedures for the operation (including effectiveness and sensitivity), routine monitoring, testing and calibration of metal detector and X-ray equipment.

The procedure will identify the individuals responsible for completing the tests.

The frequency of testing shall be based on the quantity and type(s) of product. However, the following should be considered:

- start-up and finish of shifts
- product changeovers
- change in machine settings following downtime for repairs
- customer requirements
- regular checks throughout production (these should consider the ability to recover and retest product in the event of a failure; therefore a minimum of hourly testing may typically be expected).

The testing procedures shall be based on the requirements of clause 4.10.3.5, documented and carried out by trained staff.

The results of the tests conducted shall be documented to demonstrate that all requirements of the monitoring procedure were executed and were within the correct working parameters.

4.10.3.5   Metal detector checking procedures

The company shall establish procedures for the operation, routine monitoring, testing and calibration of the metal detector. Industry best practice, manufacturers' guidelines and specific customer requirements (clause 4.10.1.3) should be considered when developing these procedures.

The procedures identified in the Standard are based on accepted best practice and should form the basis of the metal detection testing procedure.

4.10.3.6   Corrective action

There shall be procedures in place specifying the action required in the event of the detector failing a routine test (e.g. failing to detect or reject the test piece). This procedure shall form part of the training of the persons responsible for completing the tests.

The procedures shall include a combination of isolation, quarantining and re-inspection of all product produced since the last successful test.

If the cause of the failure is a system fault, the fault shall be repaired before recommencing production on the implicated line.

4.10.4 Magnets

Some sectors of the food industry (for example, grinding of cereals, coffee, etc.) employ magnets to reduce or remove metal fragments. Where these are used, it is important to document the type (e.g. electromagnet or permanent magnet), location and strength of the magnet.

Magnets are not an alternative to metal detectors but an additional control mechanism, and factories using magnets shall still comply with the requirements of clause 4.10.3.

The magnet's strength should be designed to ensure that it is sufficient to capture metal foreign bodies. A number of factors should be considered when determining the correct strength – for example: the type of product (e.g. the size of the food particles); the width of the conveyor belt, chute or other equipment in which the magnets are located; and the flow rate of the food or raw material.

Documented procedures shall be in place to ensure:

- routine inspection – for example, visual inspection for damage and the presence of captured metal fragments
- cleaning – the ability of a magnet to capture a foreign body can be hampered if dirt or other material is allowed to collect on the magnet's surface
- strength testing – for example, by using a magnetic meter (measuring the magnet's strength in tesla) or through the use of a third-party calibration service.

Records of all checks, recalibrations or servicing shall be maintained.

Good practice to monitor a magnet's performance includes locating a second 'policing' magnet as close to the first as possible. Any metal found on this second magnet indicates that the 'process' magnet is not performing satisfactorily and is failing to remove all metal particles.

4.10.5 Optical sorting equipment

Optical sorting devices are commonly used in some industries to remove unsatisfactory products or contaminants, usually on the basis of colour or variance from a reference material. Where equipment is in use, procedures need to be developed for the calibration and testing of the equipment. This is usually developed with the manufacturer when the equipment is installed and commissioned.

Records of all checks, recalibrations or servicing shall be maintained.

4.10.6 Container cleanliness – glass jars, cans and other rigid containers

4.10.6.1 Procedures

Where packaging containers are supplied to the production site in a rigid format (for example, empty cans, bottles or glass jars), there is an increased risk of contamination of the container during storage and transit before filling. Glass containers have the additional risk of damage during transit.

The site needs to consider the potential risks associated with the containers and introduce appropriate controls to reduce the risk. It is usual for such containers to be inverted and cleaned prior to use and for glass jars and bottles to be subject to automatic or, by exception, manual inspection before use.

Documented procedures, based on risk assessment, shall be available to address the potential risks.

4.10.6.2 Effectiveness of container cleaning

In-line cleaning and automatic rejection systems are not a requirement, but the use of such systems is strongly encouraged. Where systems are present, these shall be checked and records maintained of checks.

Consideration must also be made of the procedures to take in the event of a breakage occurring after cleaning. (clause 4.9.3.3).

4.11   Housekeeping and hygiene

FUNDAMENTAL

> Housekeeping and cleaning systems shall be in place which ensure appropriate standards of hygiene are maintained at all times and the risk of product contamination is minimised.

The site shall be maintained to a suitable level of cleanliness. Control of hygiene shall be achieved through schedules of cleaning and policies on housekeeping based on risk assessment. This shall be demonstrated through documented and monitored systems. The methods of cleaning themselves shall not pose a risk of product contamination (e.g. from cleaning areas adjacent to open product).

4.11.1   Documented cleaning procedures

Documented cleaning procedures shall be in place to ensure consistent and effective cleaning and as a guide for training purposes. When documenting such procedures, an emphasis should be placed on food contact equipment. Cleaning procedures need to include information on:

■   The equipment, building and plant to be cleaned.

■   Methods to be used – these shall be in sufficient detail for cleaning to be carried out to a consistently acceptable standard. In a majority of sites, good practice would normally include the six stages of cleaning as appropriate:

1.   Remove gross debris, e.g. sweep or wipe

2.   Rinse with water

3.   Wash with detergent solution using hot water

4.   Rinse

5.   Dry

6.   Sanitise.

■   Instructions on the correct/safe dismantling of equipment where this is required for cleaning purposes.

■   Frequency of cleaning.

■   Materials to be used (e.g. required chemicals and concentrations, and equipment such as hoses or brushes).

■   Staff responsible.

■   Records to be kept.

■   Responsibility for verification.

■   Method of verification (e.g. visual inspection, ATP monitoring, microbiological swabs or allergen swabs).

Where equipment requires different levels of cleaning (e.g. between products, or between daily and weekly clean), each requirement should be clearly detailed.

It may be useful to include photographs in the instructions.

The procedures need to be reviewed and updated when changes occur to the areas to be cleaned.

4.11.2   Cleaning inspection

Limits of acceptable and unacceptable cleaning performance shall be defined. The limits need to be based on the risk, and this should be used as the basis for assessing whether the cleaning undertaken is of an acceptable standard. Where the cleaning is designed principally to provide a clean processing environment, an assessment of 'visual clean' may be sufficient. Where the level of cleaning is to ensure a sterile food contact surface or to ensure that traces of allergen have been removed, the level of acceptable cleaning performance may need to be based on ATP tests, microbiological or allergen testing.

Once the acceptable limits for cleaning have been established, the cleaning procedure can be validated by checking that the specified cleaning method, cleaning chemical and concentration are capable of achieving the level of performance required. Records of validation shall be maintained.

4.11.3   Training and resources

Cleaning shall be carried out by trained personnel and records shall be maintained. Training records shall demonstrate that the relevant training has been completed. This shall cover all staff involved in cleaning activities, including agency staff.

Where specialist resources or activity are required (for example, to dismantle or enter large equipment), this shall be appropriately scheduled and, where necessary, planned for non-production periods.

Full support shall be provided by engineering, either by additional training or by having engineering staff present during cleaning operations.

4.11.4   Cleaning sign-off

An authorised member of staff (e.g. line supervisor, QA supervisor or production manager) shall formally accept equipment back into operation following an inspection, to confirm that the cleaning has been completed satisfactorily. A record shall be completed.

The results of checks on cleaning, including visual or analytical checks, shall be recorded. These records shall be used to identify trends in cleaning performance and instigate improvements where required. For example, trends and potential changes could be discussed during management meetings (clause 1.1.3).

Changes in cleaning regimes may be required to prevent the build-up of micro-organisms, biofilm or scale. Companies should demonstrate that they have access to relevant expertise or advice when required.

4.11.5   Cleaning equipment

Cleaning chemicals and equipment need to be fit for purpose. For example:

■ They shall be suitable for the purpose for which they are intended and capable of achieving the desired level of cleaning.

■ Cleaning chemicals shall be selected to prevent the risk of product tainting (e.g. phenolic and strongly scented chemicals are not suitable).

■ Equipment (such as scourers) that has the potential to shed fibres is not suitable.

Equipment and chemicals shall be clearly identified at all times. (This may include colour coding and labelling.) They shall also be stored hygienically and in a manner that prevents contamination.

Good practice would be to supply cleaning chemicals to production areas ready-diluted, for use with verified auto-dosing systems.

Equipment used for cleaning high-care or high-risk areas shall be dedicated for use in that area.

4.11.6   Cleaning in place (CIP)

4.11.6.1   Effective operation and maintenance of CIP

It shall be ensured that cleaning-in-place (CIP) facilities, where they exist, operate effectively and are monitored and maintained to ensure that the principal factors, such as cleaning-chemical concentration, temperature and duration of cleaning, are adequate.

4.11.6.2   Verification of CIP system

The schematic plan should be provided by the supplier when the system is installed and should be updated whenever a change is made.

The layout of the pipework and the position of valves, spray balls and holding tanks is essential to ensure that the system is consistently operating effectively and that there are no dead spots or areas where cross-contamination between cleaning chemicals and product can occur. Issues are most likely to occur where CIP systems are modified or extended.

The system inspection may be undertaken by a site's engineers or could be carried out as part of a service agreement with the supplier or with the service company maintaining the system. The report should include an overview of the scope of the inspection, any recommendations for improvement and confirmation or otherwise of the effectiveness of the system.

4.11.6.3   Operation of CIP equipment

The CIP process parameters and tolerances shall be specified and form a reference for checks on the CIP system. Key parameters shall be checked and recorded at a frequency based on risk, to ensure that the system is functioning correctly and achieving the level of cleaning required.

4.12   Waste/waste disposal

> **Waste disposal shall be managed in accordance with legal requirements and to prevent accumulation, risk of contamination and the attraction of pests.**

Waste disposal systems shall ensure that the risk of contamination to products is minimised through the control of cross-contamination and control of pests.

Disposal shall comply with legal requirements.

Risk assessment shall consider the movement and flow of waste. For example, bins shall be dedicated to either high-risk or low-risk areas and shall not move between the two. High-risk waste should be transferred to other containers at the high-risk transfer point.

Good practice should ensure that containers used for either raw material storage or handling, or for finished product storage, shall not be used for collecting waste. Instead, waste shall be collected in appropriate, designated waste containers.

4.12.1   Licensing and legislation

Waste contractors shall be appropriately licensed where required by local law – for example, for categorised waste.

Where legislation exists for specific waste streams, this shall be complied with. Such legislation may include requirements for segregation and categorisation.

Records of disposal shall be maintained and available for audit.

4.12.2   Food for animal feed

In many parts of the world, there are specific regulations relating to the suitability of products for inclusion in animal feed. It is essential that, where food products are supplied for animal feed, the site is aware of – and complies with – the relevant legislation.

In some countries, legislation covers particular categories of food products which cannot be used for animal feed, segregation from other waste streams and management to prevent contamination.

There are several recognised feed schemes and, where applicable, certification to such a scheme may be required.

4.12.3 External waste storage

External waste-collection containers and rooms housing waste facilities shall be managed to minimise risk. Particular consideration shall be given to:

- the pest-control implications of external waste-collection areas
- identification
- ease of cleaning
- emptying at appropriate frequencies
- keeping facilities well maintained
- keeping containers covered or doors closed.

4.12.4 Unsafe and trademarked waste

Requirements for the disposal of trademarked waste shall be defined within a contract with the waste disposal contractor and include the need for records of destruction or disposal to be maintained. The objective is to ensure that waste products do not re-enter the food supply chain once sent for disposal.

If unsafe products are transferred to a third party for destruction, the third party shall be a specialist in secure product or waste disposal and shall provide records which include the quantity of waste collected.

4.13 Pest control

> The whole site shall have an effective preventive pest control programme in place to minimise the risk of infestation and there shall be the resources available to rapidly respond to any issues which occur to prevent risk to products.

Control of pests shall be undertaken at a level commensurate with the needs of the whole site, based on: the nature of identified potential pests; the characteristics of raw materials, equipment, finished products, process, site and environment; and the potential for future pest risks.

Where instances of pest ingress (i.e. single occasion or low numbers) occur, these need to be appropriately investigated and actioned but shall not be deemed as loss of control. However, where pest infestation (i.e. evidence of pests breeding within the building or site over a period of time) occurs, this shall be regarded as loss of control and a lack of maintenance of the pest control programme, and will lead to a major non-conformity being awarded.

BRC Global Standards publishes a separate *Best Practice Guideline on Pest Control*, which is available from www.brcbookshop.com.

4.13.1 Pest control system

There shall be regular inspection and treatment of the site to deter or eradicate infestation. The frequency of inspection and treatment of premises shall be based on the product risk and the age, design and location of buildings and equipment.

Pest control is often contracted to external companies, which may need to be licensed or approved by local or national authorities. The contractor shall demonstrate competence (evidence could, for example, include membership of a national trade association, training records or a third-party audit).

The service contract shall be clearly defined and should include provision for additional treatments where required to eradicate any infestation that may occur.

Where pest control is handled in house, responsible employees shall have appropriate training, as evidenced by training records (clause 4.13.2).

4.13.2   In-house pest control

A site conducting its own pest control shall demonstrate that:

- Staff are trained with sufficient knowledge to select appropriate pest control chemicals and proofing methods, and understand their limitations of use, relevant to the biology of the pests associated with the site. The auditor will check that the appropriate training record(s) demonstrate that sufficient training has taken place.

- Sufficient resources (for example, financial, manpower or access to external resources) are available to respond to any infestation issues.

- Specialist technical knowledge (for example, in the form of an external contractor) can be obtained.

- The site has an up-to-date understanding of current legislation governing the use of pest control products. (It should be noted that in some geographic regions this legislation is updated frequently and the appointed staff will need to remain up to date.)

- There must be dedicated locked facilities for the storage of pest control products.

4.13.3   Pest control documentation and records

Written procedures and inspection documentation shall be maintained. These shall include:

- an up-to-date site plan identifying the locations of pest control devices, signed and authorised by an appropriate person (this plan should be reviewed periodically, e.g. annually or when there are site changes)

- identification (e.g. a numbered list) of the types of baits and monitoring devices on site

- details of the pest control products used and instructions for their safe and effective use

- clearly defined responsibilities for site management and the contractor (e.g. methods of communication, such as a nominated site and contractor contact, and details of when review meetings will take place)

- records of any pest activity observed

- details of pest control activities undertaken.

All pest control inspections shall be recorded, even where there are only negative findings to report.

4.13.4   Bait stations

Bait stations shall be robust, tamper-resistant and secured in place to limit the potential for contamination. Their design and use must not contaminate the products (for example, bait stations should contain non-spill formulations). They shall also be appropriately located, as advised by the pest control specialist.

Rodent bait is generally toxic, so shall be controlled to avoid contamination. Toxic rodent bait shall not be used within production or storage areas where open product is present except when treating an active infestation.

4.13.5   Fly killing

Where fly-killing devices and/or pheromone traps are used, they shall be correctly sited and operational. If there is the potential for insects to be expelled from a fly-killing device and contaminate the product, alternative systems and equipment shall be used (e.g. those based on sticky-board technology) or the devices shall be moved to a more appropriate position.

Equipment shall be fully operational. For example, bulbs on fly-killing devices shall be changed at regular intervals (generally annually) to maintain optimal luminosity performance, and pheromone traps shall be replenished quarterly or in accordance with the manufacturer's instructions. Documentation shall provide evidence of this maintenance.

4.13.6   Infestation

In the event of infestation, immediate action shall be taken to eliminate the hazard.

This may include identifying and quarantining any potentially affected product so that it can be evaluated in accordance with the site's non-conforming-product procedures.

Action may also include steps to protect other products and inspection by the pest control specialist.

Any such infestation and corrective actions shall be recorded.

4.13.7 Records of pest control inspections

Records of pest control will include any recommendations made by the pest control specialist (for example, changes to inspection frequency or pest proofing).

It is the responsibility of the company to ensure that all relevant recommendations made by the pest control specialist are carried out within a suitable timescale and verified for effectiveness. Records of these changes shall be maintained.

4.13.8 Pest control survey

An in-depth, documented pest control survey shall be completed periodically. These surveys are in addition to the regular inspections (e.g. monthly checks of bait and traps) conducted as part of the pest control programme (clause 4.13.1).

The aim of these surveys is an in-depth examination of the pest control activities, to ensure that they remain appropriate and to allow an in-depth assessment of the site and equipment for evidence of activity. Where stored product insects represent a potential hazard, the visits should be scheduled for a time when access to equipment for inspection purposes is available, so that the greatest value can be gained from the survey.

The review will be completed by a pest control expert – for example, the pest control contractor's field biologist.

Typically, this survey is completed quarterly. However, risk assessment may indicate that a different frequency is required. For example, where products are produced seasonally or the pest issues are seasonal in nature, less frequent visits may be appropriate.

The results should be incorporated into the company management review (clause 1.1.3).

This clause applies to all sites, not just those carrying out their own pest control.

4.13.9 Periodic assessment

There shall be a periodic assessment of pest control inspections, including results and trends. The review will consider:

- pest control measures
- review of bait takes
- catch analysis from trapping devices
- identification of any trends
- review of action taken
- recommendations for changes or improvement.

As a minimum, this shall be conducted annually and in the event of an infestation.

4.14 Storage facilities

All facilities used for the storage of ingredients, in-process product and finished products shall be suitable for its purpose.

The site's procedures for storage shall be controlled to ensure they do not pose a risk to products. This includes all raw materials and packaging, intermediates and finished products.

4.14.1   Documented storage procedures

The company shall consider the potential risks to product safety and quality that may develop during storage. Documented procedures shall be developed to minimise the risks to products, intermediates and raw materials. This may include:

- managing the transfer of chilled and frozen products between temperature-controlled areas

- maintaining the cleanliness of storage areas (e.g. with appropriate cleaning procedures and identified frequencies, as evidenced by documented records)

- appropriate segregation to avoid cross-contamination (e.g. physical, microbiological or allergen) or taint uptake

- storing materials off the floor and away from walls to allow cleaning and inspection

- specific handling or storage instructions to prevent product damage.

Relevant staff shall be trained in these procedures.

4.14.2   Temperature control

Where temperature control (i.e. ensuring products are appropriately stored) is required, the storage area shall be capable of maintaining the required level.

Temperature management is usually carried out through the use of automatic temperature-recording systems, which raise an alarm where temperatures are outside a set range for a defined period, i.e. to allow for the usual defrost cycles. The alarm must be capable of notifying a responsible person even outside of normal working hours, whether by notification to on-site security, by a home call or by ring-through to a service centre.

Where such automatic systems are not in use, the same level of safeguard to product temperature control needs to be instigated through manual temperature checks. To achieve a similar level of control, it is expected that manual temperature checks would be carried out on a 4-hourly basis, including during evenings and weekends. The frequency of checks could be reduced where the nature of the product and the insulating capability of the unit are such that the product would remain unaffected by a refrigeration failure of longer than 4 hours (for example, with some frozen products). Ongoing temperature records shall be in place to demonstrate that product temperature requirements are met. Procedures shall specify the frequency of manual checks or the use of automatic continual monitoring systems. All temperature monitoring shall allow intervention before product temperatures exceed defined limits for the safety, legality or quality of products.

4.14.3   Storage in controlled atmosphere

Where storage conditions include other parameters (for example, modified-atmosphere storage of fruit and vegetables), the mix of gases needs to be defined and monitored to ensure the quality of the product is managed.

It should be noted that these are tests to ensure that the correct composition of gases is present. They are, therefore, different from the tests identified in clause 4.5.4, which relate to contamination and food safety.

4.14.4   Storage outside

Where it is necessary to store product and equipment outside, these shall be protected from pests and the elements. Particular attention must be paid to cleaning and inspection of the materials before use to prevent contamination.

4.14.5   Stock rotation

Stock, whether raw materials, intermediate or finished products, shall be controlled to ensure that products do not exceed their shelf life. This control is generally operated on a 'first in, first out' basis. Receipt documents and/or product identification, such as labelling, will help to facilitate correct order in relation to the products' manufacturing dates and prescribed shelf life.

4.15   Dispatch and transport

Procedures shall be in place to ensure that the management of dispatch and of the vehicles and containers used for transporting products from the site do not present a risk to the safety or quality of the products.

The site's procedures for dispatch and transport shall be controlled to ensure they do not pose a risk to final products.

4.15.1   Documented dispatch and transport procedures

The company shall consider the potential risks to product safety and quality that may develop during dispatch and transport. Documented procedures shall be developed to minimise identified risks. This may include consideration of:

- controlling temperature on loading-dock areas
- a requirement for vehicles to be loaded/unloaded in covered bays
- securing of loads on pallets to prevent movement during transit
- vehicle inspections prior to loading and unloading.

4.15.2   Traceability records

There shall be records showing the movement of finished product both into and out of the dispatch area, in order to demonstrate effective management of that area and ensure that traceability is maintained.

4.15.3   Vehicle inspection

Vehicle inspections shall be completed prior to loading and unloading to confirm that vehicles are suitable for use. Inspection of vehicles should be a site responsibility even where the vehicles and distribution are subcontracted. As a minimum, this will consider:

- correct levels of cleanliness
- freedom from strong odours which could taint a product
- maintenance to prevent product damage during transit
- correct operating temperatures.

Records of inspections shall be maintained.

4.15.4   Vehicle temperature control

Vehicles that are temperature controlled shall demonstrate the control of temperature under both minimum and maximum load. This can be achieved through the use of temperature recorders, data loggers or manual recorded checks. Where manual checks are used, the frequency must ensure that the safety or quality of the product is not in doubt. The use of data loggers may be considered as a verification method.

Planned maintenance programmes and calibration records shall be documented.

4.15.5   Vehicle maintenance and hygiene

Documented hygiene and maintenance procedures for all vehicles (e.g. forklift trucks, pallet trucks) and equipment (e.g. loading hoses for silos) shall be in place.

These shall include:

- the method(s) of cleaning
- the frequency with which the cleaning must be completed
- records that the cleaning has been completed.

4.15.6   Transport procedures

The site shall have documented procedures for the transport of products, including:

- The identification of any restrictions for mixed loads – for example, to avoid cross-contamination or taint uptake (e.g. specifying where allergen-free materials are to be stored or transported).

- All finished products in transport shall be secure to ensure they cannot be contaminated, either accidentally or deliberately. This may include tamper-evident packing, vehicle seals, or contractual handling arrangements with transport providers (including, for example, not leaving vehicles unattended in insecure situations).

- Temperature-controlled vehicles shall have documented breakdown procedures (in case of, for example, vehicle breakdown or failure of the refrigeration system). These shall consider:
    - facility for vehicle drivers to easily contact the company or haulier for assistance
    - provision of a back-up vehicle or rapid repair facility
    - guidelines to evaluate the acceptability of product affected by the breakdown.

The appropriate staff shall be trained in these procedures.

4.15.7   Third-party contractors

Where the company uses a third party for storage, all of the requirements specified in this section shall be communicated to that third party. They will be clearly defined in the contract and verified (for example, by a supplier audit).

Alternatively, the third party shall be certificated to the *Global Standard for Storage and Distribution* or a similar internationally recognised standard.

5   Product Control

5.1   Product design/development

> Product design and development procedures shall be in place for new products or processes and any changes to product, packaging or manufacturing processes to ensure that safe and legal products are produced.

5.1.1   New product development

The objective of this clause is to ensure that the product development activities are aligned with any site policies on the types of product or hazards handled on site to prevent the introduction of hazards. Typically, this applies where companies have policies to exclude particular allergens (for instance, nuts) from the site. Any such restrictions shall be documented. Where no restrictions apply, this need not be documented.

5.1.2   Approval of HACCP for new products

Experience has shown that sometimes only minor changes to ingredients, packaging or process conditions can have a significant effect on the safety of products. The sign-off of changes by the HACCP team leader or an authorised HACCP team member is designed to ensure that the consequences of any change are understood. This can be demonstrated by a record of sign-off of product changes, e.g. a change authorisation form. Records should be available even where the change is shown not to result in any modification to the existing HACCP plan.

The sign-off shall occur before the products are introduced into the factory, i.e. sign-off is completed before factory trials to ensure that new risks (for instance, from allergens) are not introduced into the factory.

5.1.3   Factory trials

Documented evidence of production trials (i.e. not kitchen-scale trials) needs to be available, together with test results validating that the product formulation and manufacturing processes are capable of producing a safe product of the desired quality. Samples to validate the shelf life should be taken from these trials.

Factory trials may not be required where new products are very closely based on existing products. Where production trials are not undertaken, the reason must be documented.

5.1.4   Shelf-life evaluation

The company shall establish a documented procedure detailing how shelf-life trials are undertaken. This procedure shall consider the handling conditions throughout the supply chain, e.g. chilled products are often subject to 2 hours at an ambient temperature mid-life to mimic the conditions during retail shopping. The aim of shelf-life trials is to confirm that product safety, legality and quality are acceptable throughout the shelf life.

Where long-shelf-life products (for example, some canned or frozen products) are developed, it may not be possible to complete full shelf-life trials. The justification for the declared shelf life shall be documented and based on experience from similar products and science-based justification.

5.1.5   Legality of labels

The labelling of products must meet all of the legal requirements for the country of sale. The site will be expected to demonstrate how they keep up to date with labelling legislation and the process for reviewing and signing off labels for new products and wherever changes to products occur.

Where a customer has responsibility for the final label, the site shall be responsible for supplying accurate information on which to base the label information.

The site should have a procedure for undertaking a legality check and sign-off of proofs for new labels to ensure their legality.

5.1.6   Nutritional claims

Where a particular claim about the formulation of a product has been made, procedures must be in place to validate that the claim is correct and to ensure that, when handling the product during processing, contamination that affects the claim cannot occur.

Good practice is to ensure that a programme of ongoing verification is in place to demonstrate that claims are consistently being met.

Claims such as 'free from' need particular care to ensure that cross-contamination does not occur during processing. Where there are particular legislative requirements relating to claims such as low fat, sugar or salt, the requirements must be understood and must be met.

5.2   Management of allergens

FUNDAMENTAL

> **The company shall have a developed system for the management of allergenic materials which minimises the risk of allergen contamination of products and meets legal requirements for labelling.**

Legislation in many countries requires that the presence of food allergens, when deliberately present in a product, must be declared on pack.

In addition to the deliberate use of allergenic ingredients in a food, there are occasions when a product can be cross-contaminated due to the supply chain or manufacturing environments. Where there is a genuine risk of cross-contamination with an allergen, this must be managed to minimise both its likelihood and the levels that are likely to be present.

Consideration must be given to the specific legislative requirements in the geographic origin of the raw material, in the country of manufacture and in the country of destination (i.e. where the product will be sold to the final consumer). For example, the list of substances that are considered to be allergenic is different in Europe, the USA, Australia and Japan.

Where products are both produced and sold in countries where there are no legal requirements for the labelling of allergens, the list of allergens as defined in the *Codex General Standard for the Labelling of Prepackaged Foods* (section 4.2.1.4) should be used as the basis when assessing compliance to the requirements set out in the Standard.

Research is being conducted in a number of countries, including the UK and Australia, to identify thresholds (i.e. the minimum amount of an allergen that will cause a reaction in the majority of allergic customers). This research may, in due course, provide useful data that can be combined with other risk-assessment tools. At the current time, however, this data has not been fully evaluated or published. Early indications are that the values will be very low (e.g. a few milligrams) and factories will need to continue to use the full range of risk-assessment and management tools to ensure they continue to produce products that are safe for allergenic consumers.

5.2.1   Raw material assessment

Raw materials are a potential source of allergens and of cross-contamination. Therefore, part of the supplier approval and raw-material risk-assessment procedures (clause 3.5.1) shall assess raw materials for the presence of allergens and the potential for contamination.

Raw material specifications (including flavourings, additives, carriers and processing aids) must be agreed with each raw material supplier and include the allergen status (both content and risk of cross-contamination) of the materials.

Where required, additional allergen information shall be obtained – for example, through the use of supplier questionnaires or audits.

Where a compound raw material (i.e. one manufactured from a number of ingredients) is purchased, the risk assessment must consider the risks associated with the raw material, its ingredients and the manufacturing sites of the ingredients.

The assessment process and the outcome of the assessment must be documented.

5.2.2   List of allergenic materials

All materials that contain allergenic substances (ingredients, processing aids, intermediates and finished products) shall be listed in a single reference document.

The aim of this clause is to ensure that the site maintains up-to-date knowledge of the allergens that are handled on the site, as well as current information from raw material suppliers.

The need to maintain an up-to-date list should be communicated to all areas which can introduce new allergens onto the site – for example, new product development.

5.2.3   Risk assessment for cross-contamination

A risk-assessment process shall be completed to identify potential routes of cross-contamination. Consideration shall be given to:

- The physical state of the allergen. For example:
    - Powdered ingredients represent a greater risk of aerial cross-contamination than those in liquid form.
    - Sticky or fatty ingredients are likely to adhere to surfaces should cleaning be ineffective.
    - Particulates (such as pieces of nut) may result in significant heterogeneous contamination.

- Identification of potential points of cross-contamination. An 'Allergen Process Flow' diagram or 'Allergen Map' can be useful in understanding where allergenic ingredients and foods exist in the plant and where they are introduced into the process. This usually takes the form of a site plan, on which are highlighted all the routes each allergenic material can take. This map can subsequently be used to identify areas where cross-contamination between allergenic and non-allergenic materials (ingredients, intermediates or products) can occur. (The map should consider process flow, environmental factors, production activities, shared equipment and people.)

- Assessment of the risk at each stage identified in the previous step.

- Identification and implementation of all reasonable controls to reduce or eliminate cross-contamination – for example, segregation, the use of dedicated lines or equipment, enhanced cleaning schedules, etc.

The risk-assessment process, the assessments and any resulting procedures or factory controls must be documented.

5.2.4   Cross-contamination procedures

The risk assessment (clause 5.2.3) shall be used to develop the factory controls and procedures for handling raw materials, intermediates and finished products to reduce (and, where possible, remove) the risk of cross-contamination.

Procedures shall be implemented even where on-pack warning labels (clause 5.2.6) are used.

Particular attention should be given to:

- Physical segregation – ideally, allergenic ingredients and products will be totally segregated from non-allergenic ingredients and products. This could involve, for example, dedicated storage areas, dedicated (and colour-coded) production equipment, and the use of dedicated production lines.

- Time segregation – where products must be handled in the same factory areas or on the same production lines, consideration should be given to the use of time segregation. For example, all non-allergen products could be produced first and allergenic materials introduced subsequently, or the use of allergenic materials could be confined to the end of a day/shift and only before a full clean. Production scheduling can also be used to minimise the frequency of changeovers between allergen-containing and non-allergen-containing products – for example, in some factories it is possible to limit the use of nuts to a defined period or shift, rather than producing nut-containing products throughout the week.

- Protective clothing must not be a source of allergen contamination. Consideration should, therefore, be given to the use of separate clothing or overalls for handling allergenic materials. It is normally useful to colour-code protective clothing to prevent confusion.

- The use of dedicated equipment or utensils – these should be clearly identifiable (e.g. by colour coding).

- A number of allergens can form fine powders (e.g. flour, milk powder and soya isolates). The movement of airborne dust should be minimised – for example, by using physical barriers (such as shrouds, lids or segregated areas) for dispensing and mixing operations. Consideration should also be given to the location of air-conditioning outlets or the use of fans to ensure these do not distribute airborne allergens.

- Waste-handling and spillage controls should be considered to ensure that allergens are removed efficiently and that the removal process does not become the source of allergen contamination in other areas of the factory.

- Consideration should be given to the allergens that may be handled in non-production areas of the site – for example, in canteens or in new product development. A policy for food brought onto site by staff, or used in vending machines or catering facilities, should be developed. The policy may ban certain allergens or restrict them to certain areas of the site.

Where colour coding is used, consideration shall be given to the choice of colours, to ensure that colour-blind staff are able to identify the correct items.

5.2.5   Rework

Specific documented procedures will operate to prevent rework containing allergens from being used in products or processes that do not contain those allergens.

Best practice is that rework is used on a 'like-for-like' basis, i.e. it is used only in exactly the same product.

The use of rework must be documented.

5.2.6   On-pack warning labels

Where controls cannot prevent cross-contamination and there is a significant and genuine risk of the presence of an allergen(s) that would not otherwise be present and is therefore not mentioned elsewhere on the product (for example, in the ingredients list), the use of on-pack advisory labels shall be considered.

The use of a warning label should be justifiable on the basis of the risk assessment (clauses 5.2.3 and 5.2.4) and should not be a substitute for good manufacturing practices.

Reference shall be made to national legislation, guidelines or codes of practice when making such a statement, to ensure that best practice is followed. For example, consideration should be given to:

- the location of the warning (preferably in close proximity to the ingredients list)

- the visibility of the statement – colour, location and font size can all aid consumers

- the choice of the warning phrase used, so that the meaning is clear to consumers.

5.2.7   Allergen claims

Allergic, food-intolerant or sensitive individuals are likely to actively seek and choose products that claim to be suitable for them to consume (for example 'gluten-free' products). It is, therefore, essential that any allergen claim is based on rigorous controls to ensure its validity and continuous implementation.

Where a claim is made regarding the suitability of a food, full validation and verification activities will be required to ensure that the claim is consistently met. Typically, this will include:

- demonstration that production processes are in place to ensure the product does not contain traces of the allergen

- analysis of the final product

- assessment of the adequacy of cleaning, as detailed in clause 5.2.8 (where the site also produces products containing the allergen about which the claim is made, additional verification controls will be required)

- raw material controls – in addition to the normal requirements listed in clause 5.2.1, additional validation/ verification requirements are likely to be needed (for example, raw material testing, additional supplier questionnaires, site audits, etc.).

The validation and verification activities shall be recorded.

5.2.8   Allergen cleaning regimes

Some standard cleaning regimes will be insufficient to ensure the removal of all allergenic material. Therefore, specific cleaning procedures shall be present on site where allergen-containing materials require control.

Cleaning procedures should be designed to remove or reduce to acceptable levels any allergenic material. Consideration should be given to:

- cleaning schedules (i.e. when cleaning will be completed)

- scheduling sufficient time to fully complete the clean to the required standard

- ensuring that cleaning instructions contain all the information required

- the order in which cleaning must be performed (i.e. to ensure that cleaning does not move an allergen into a previously cleaned area).

Where multiple allergens are handled on site, consideration should be given to whether all allergens can be managed by the same cleaning/validation/verification activities. For example, peanut, milk and sesame may need different controls due to their different physical characteristics. They may also be used on different equipment/lines, again requiring separate consideration.

The effectiveness of the procedures shall be validated. The validation shall be documented and evidence may include:

- Worst-case production/cleaning trials – all equipment, processes and allergens need to be considered.

- Targeted test locations – consider food contact surfaces, difficult-to-clean areas, deadlegs, etc.

- Targeted samples – worst-case samples should be identified for laboratory testing using suitably sensitive test methods. (Validation tests should be accredited methods and, wherever possible, quantifiable. Rapid tests, ATP and lateral flow devices are good for verification activities but are not suitable for validation.) Possible samples include the first product manufactured in the next production run, rinse water from cleaning systems, swabs, etc.

- Assessment of new equipment for ease of cleaning prior to purchase.

It is likely that validation data will need to be collected from several production runs to ensure it is representative and complete.

A number of best-practice guidelines have been published on the validation of cleaning – for example, Campden BRI Guideline 59: *Validation of cleaning to remove food allergens*.

The cleaning procedures shall be routinely verified (and, if necessary, corrective action completed) – for example, by:

- visual inspections and documented sign-off

- inclusion in internal audits

- the use of swabs or testing (e.g. rapid tests, ATP, lateral flow devices or laboratory tests).

Records shall be maintained of validation and verification checks and activities. Corrective actions shall also be recorded.

5.2.9   Allergen training

All personnel (including all temporary staff and contractors) involved in handling ingredients, equipment, utensils, packaging and products must receive training to raise awareness of food allergens and the specific allergen measures used by the company.

The level of training should be appropriate to the individual's role. For example, junior staff may require only a general understanding of the importance of allergens (information that could be included as part of the induction process), plus any specific procedures in which they are involved. However, the technical team will require greater detail.

Training records must be kept.

5.2.10   Packaging controls

Mis-packs and errors on packaging remain the most common causes of allergen withdrawals and recalls. Procedures must therefore be in place to ensure that products are packed into correct and accurate packaging.

Documented checks shall be in place to ensure that the labels applied to products are correct. For example, good practice requires that:

- label approval procedures include a check that all on-pack allergen labelling and ingredients are correct

- every batch of incoming labels is reviewed on receipt to ensure accuracy of labelling

- a risk assessment is completed on all packaging and label suppliers to ensure that adequate controls are in place at all points of packaging manufacture (for example, checks to prevent mixed-splice spools or mixed packs of cartons)

- there are procedures to monitor, document and verify that the correct labels are in use during manufacture – for example, checks at line start-up and at product changeovers must be implemented and audited regularly.

Records of the checks shall be maintained.

5.3   Provenance, assured status and claims of identity preserved materials

> Systems of traceability, identification and segregation of raw materials, intermediate and finished products shall be in place to ensure that all claims relating to provenance or assured status can be substantiated.

The objective of this clause is to ensure that all claims relating to the raw materials used in products can be substantiated and that the BRC audit process provides a suitable evaluation of the site's management of the chain of custody, where claims are made relating to primary agricultural schemes such as GLOBALGAP.

The types of claims covered by this section relate to the provenance of an ingredient or ingredients used in a product and which differentiate that ingredient from the norm. Such a claim may be made either on the product label for the consumer or in business-to-business communication. The types of claims which are covered by this clause include:

- varietal claims, e.g. Basmati rice, Aberdeen Angus beef, Bramley apples and cod fish cakes

- origin claims, e.g. Madagascan vanilla and Florida grapefruit

- assurance claims, e.g. GLOBALGAP, Red Tractor, Marine Stewardship, Dolphin-Friendly Tuna and Sustainable Palm Oil

- identity-preserved claims, e.g. Genetically Modified Organism (GMO) free.

Whilst many of the same principles apply, this clause is not intended to endorse the requirements of other certification schemes which have specific rules covering production processes at the factory – for example, organic, halal or kosher products.

Claims which relate to the composition of the product (e.g. nutritional claims, fat free, reduced sugar, etc.) are covered in clause 5.1.6.

5.3.1   Status verification of raw materials

It is the responsibility of the site to make reasonable checks to ensure that the raw materials supplied are genuine and that claims made about the ingredients are proven.

For many assurance schemes, such as GLOBALGAP, it is possible to check on a database the assurance status of the supplier and the scope of products included. Reliance solely on a declaration from a supplier will not be sufficient.

Where claims relate to variety/species (for example, varieties of fruit), examination of visual characteristics may suffice. However, for claims where visual analysis is not possible (for instance, block frozen fish), certificates of analysis and periodic sample analysis will be required.

5.3.2   Traceability

Full traceability records must be maintained, as required in clause 3.9. The records must also include details of the quantities used at each step, to enable a mass balance exercise to be undertaken.

In the absence of particular scheme requirements, the site must undertake at least every 6 months a mass balance traceability test on typical products for which a provenance claim is made. This shall ensure that the system of records maintained enables all finished product batches to be identified for a particular batch of raw materials and that, for a given finished product, the batch(es) of raw materials used for its production can be identified. The test shall be carried out in both directions. The ingredient(s) selected for the mass balance must include the ingredient for which a claim is made.

The objective is to test the systems and, where necessary, make improvements to information recording, to allow claims to be substantiated should they be challenged by a customer or legal authority. It follows that, where very different traceability systems are used within, for instance, a complex or multiproduct site, more than one mass balance traceability exercise may be required each 6 months to ensure that all systems are working effectively. However, where a site has multiple claims, it is not intended that every claim be mass balance tested every 6 months but that a representative selection of claims are chosen.

If, as part of the requirements for a particular scheme to use a logo, there is a requirement for more frequent mass balance traceability exercises, then that scheme's requirements must be met.

5.3.3   Preventing mixing or loss of identity

The process flow diagram used within the HACCP process may be used as the basis for demonstrating compliance with this clause and the requirement may be covered within the general HACCP study. The site must identify (for instance, as a list or on the process flow) potential areas where mixing of products or loss of identity may occur. Procedures of working or changes in process flow must be introduced to reduce the risk of mistakes and false claims being made.

For example: in a large pack-house packing both farm-assured and non-farm-assured fruit, the farm-assured fruit is always stored separately within dedicated cold stores. Grading and packing operations are organised so that packing of farm-assured product occurs first or on particular packing lines.

5.4   Product packaging

> Product packaging shall be appropriate for the intended use and shall be stored under conditions to minimise contamination and deterioration.

5.4.1   Compliance with legislative requirements

There have been incidences of product recalls which have resulted from a lack of communication between the supplier of the packaging materials and the food manufacturer, typically where a packaging material has been used in extreme product conditions or where packaging not designed for direct food contact has been used (for example, a plastic liner is removed from a product carton to reduce costs).

The company must be able to demonstrate that each item of product packaging meets legal requirements for its use, e.g. compliance with food contact regulations in the country of sale. This may be in the form of specifications, migration data or certificate of conformity. Where a declaration of conformity is used, any limitations on usage must be stated (e.g. the food types or storage conditions: ambient, chilled or frozen).

The supplier of the packaging must be made aware of the conditions under which the packaging is going to be used, so that the suitability of the packaging materials can be confirmed. This may take the form of a specification provided to the packaging supplier and would include as appropriate:

■ contact with food – direct food contact or, where not used for direct food contact, the nature of the barrier layer

■ characteristics of the food – any adverse characteristics of the food which may increase migration of chemicals from the packaging (e.g. high fat content, or low or high product pH)

■ conditions of processing – for example, high-temperature fill, thermal processing in pack, or freezing

■ expected customer usage – for example, microwave in pack, cooking in pack, or freezing.

5.4.2   Protection from contamination

In order to avoid product contamination risks from packaging (such as glass) or contamination of unused packaging by products, packaging should be stored away from raw materials and finished product. This may be achieved by use of a dedicated packaging store or a dedicated area of a raw material store. Only packaging required for immediate use should be stored in the actual packing area.

The storage of packaging outside is only acceptable where the packaging material:

■ is not at risk of deterioration, e.g. rusting of cans

■ is protected from contamination

■ is cleaned effectively before filling.

Once packing has finished, controls shall be in place to ensure that any 'leftover' packaging is still suitable for use before return to storage, e.g. that it has not been contaminated or printed with code information preventing reuse. Any open containers shall be appropriately resealed or rewrapped and returned to appropriate storage to minimise potential for contamination (e.g. splashing during cleaning operations) or mis-packs. It is necessary to ensure that traceability of packaging is retained, e.g. that coding is included on the outer packs on return to storage.

Where changes to packaging (for instance, changes in labelling information) occur, any obsolete packaging shall be removed from the packaging storage area and clearly identified to prevent accidental use.

5.4.3   Product contact liners

Packaging materials used, for instance, as liners for containers, as covers for work in progress or as bags for prepared ingredients, may themselves be a source of contamination. Such packaging materials shall be visually distinct from product, e.g. blue or red and of a sufficient thickness to reduce the potential for ripping or being damaged.

The requirements apply to materials purchased by the company. However, suppliers of ingredients should also be strongly encouraged to supply ingredients in accordance with these requirements to reduce the risk of packaging contaminating products.

Where companies are producing products for further processing, clear liners should not be used as they present a potential hazard for the next manufacturer.

This clause does not apply to packaging used for sale to the final consumer.

5.5 Product inspection and laboratory testing

The company shall undertake or subcontract inspection and analyses which are critical to confirm product safety, legality and quality, using appropriate procedures, facilities and standards.

5.5.1 Product inspection and testing

5.5.1.1 Product test schedules

The company needs to have a documented schedule of tests which are carried out both on the products and on the processing environment.

The objective of product tests is to ensure that products are manufactured to specification and in compliance with safety and legislative requirements. The HACCP study is likely to identify some of the tests required and their frequency. However, consideration must be given to other tests which ensure the quality of the product and which may not have been included within the HACCP study. The frequency and type of product tests should be based on risk and on any particular customer requirements. The site is expected to be able to explain and justify the basis for the frequency of tests with reference to historical or scientific information as appropriate.

The test method and specifications for each test shall be documented. Where the results of a test are not quantitative (for instance, bake colour, texture or organoleptic tests), colour standards or reference samples shall be used as appropriate to provide a reference point for test results, i.e. to define pass/fail criteria.

The schedule of tests shall include environmental monitoring of the processing environment/equipment – for instance, microbiological swab tests, ATP monitoring tests or settle plates appropriate to the type of processing activity and the risks to the product.

5.5.1.2 Reviewing test results

Systems of recording and review shall be formalised and shall include evidence of actions taken on identified trends, or where unsatisfactory results are recorded.

The use of graphs or charts of test results provides a good method of identifying trends and anomalous results.

5.5.1.3 Shelf-life verification

Companies are expected to have a programme of ongoing shelf-life evaluation across their range of products or product types. To achieve this, samples should be retained from some or all production runs.

Records shall be available supporting the declared shelf life for each product or group of similar products. These may include microbiological and sensory analysis, as well as relevant chemical factors such as pH and a_w. Records shall include, as appropriate, shelf-life trials extending beyond the stated life of the product to ensure a margin of safety.

Where products have long shelf lives (for instance, some canned products), the shelf life should be based on similar products and take into account any particular features of the new product. The justification for the shelf life must be documented.

5.5.2   Laboratory testing

5.5.2.1 Pathogen testing facilities

The requirements apply specifically to the propagation of pathogens and not to general microbiological tests such as those for yeasts and moulds, total viable count (TVC) or coliforms, which, whilst needing to be carefully controlled, present a lower level of risk.

If pathogen testing facilities are not carefully managed, a risk could be presented to products. Pathogen testing also tends to be a specialised activity, requiring specific facilities, and consequently it is usually outsourced to a specialist laboratory.

Where pathogen testing is carried out on the production site, the test facility must be physically segregated from production areas. The company shall have documented procedures to prevent product contamination and shall be able to justify the controls in place. Consideration must be given to the design of the laboratory to segregate pathogen-handling areas within the laboratory, the operation of drainage and ventilation systems, access and movement of personnel, obtaining and disposal of materials, and sample collection.

5.5.2.2   Design of laboratory facilities

If a laboratory is present within the site, documented control procedures are required to eliminate potential risks to product safety. These include: building design (particularly the design and operation of drainage and ventilation systems); how personnel move around the facility; and control of access and security. Working procedures shall ensure that protective clothing arrangements are suitable, and there shall be procedures for obtaining product samples and disposal of waste. Accreditation to ISO 17025, or a similar recognised national standard with equivalent requirements, will demonstrate that the laboratory meets these requirements.

5.5.2.3   Subcontracted laboratories

The requirements apply to tests which are critical to product safety or legality. Results from such tests must be credible and may be called upon in a court of law.

The company needs to identify which tests are critical to product safety or legality, such as compliance with label claims/declarations (e.g. nutritional claims, alcohol content) and tests for contamination (e.g. pesticides, aflatoxins).

Note that whilst the laboratory itself may have accreditation, the actual test methods used must also be accredited. Any method of analysis used that is not accredited needs justification as to why it was used – for example, it may be a method for which no accreditation is yet available.

Where critical tests are carried out by non-accredited laboratories (either contracted or on-site laboratories), there shall be suitable documentary assurances that the laboratory is working to the requirements and principles of ISO 17025. This shall include confirmation of the laboratory's procedures to meet the following general principles:

- staff competency and documented training
- test methodology – documented and based on accepted standards
- equipment – fit for purpose and appropriately calibrated
- documented QA programme, including paired testing, ring testing, etc.
- internal audits of the laboratory's operation.

On-site laboratories will be expected to demonstrate that they have a copy of ISO 17025.

5.5.2.4   Management of tests not critical to safety and legality

This requirement applies to non-critical product testing. Whilst such tests need not be carried out by a laboratory accredited to ISO 17025, it is nonetheless important that the results can be relied upon. The clause sets out the documented procedures which shall be in place to provide confidence in reliability.

5.6   Product release

> The company shall ensure that finished product is not released unless all agreed procedures have been followed.

The company shall have a process to ensure that finished product is not released from its control until all production checks have been completed and reviewed. Completion of end product testing may not be applicable prior to the release of all products. (An example would be microbiological checks on short-shelf-life products such as sandwiches.) However, there shall be appropriate checks on the CCPs to ensure that the process was within specification before product is released from the company's control. This allows product to be held where a review of the process checks identifies a potential problem.

5.6.1   Management of positive release

Where products are held either on or off site awaiting positive release, there need to be documented procedures describing the process for release and who authorises the release. The procedures need to be sufficiently robust so that accidental release cannot occur – for example, using a computerised system with password control to prevent picking of held product, or using the physical identification of pallets in the warehouse.

Process Control

6.1   Control of operations

FUNDAMENTAL

> The company shall operate to documented procedures and/or work instructions that ensure the production of consistently safe and legal product with the desired quality characteristics, in full compliance with the HACCP food safety plan.

The principle of these requirements is to ensure that the documented HACCP food safety plan is put into operation on a day-to-day basis, together with effective procedures to ensure that product can be produced consistently to the specified quality.

6.1.1   Documented work instructions

Documented process specifications, procedures or work instructions shall be available for all key stages of the operation. These documents shall be readily available to staff in the area in which the activity is undertaken. The documents shall be sufficient to ensure that all key process parameters are specified and controlled, thereby ensuring that manufactured product consistently meets safety and quality specifications. As a minimum, these documents shall cover:

- recipes – it is important that recipes are in accordance with product specifications
- mixing instructions (including speed, time, etc.)
- equipment process settings – to ensure that equipment is set up correctly for the specific product in production
- cooking times and temperatures
- cooling times and temperatures
- labelling instructions, e.g. particular requirements for label positioning on pack
- coding and shelf-life marking
- all CCPs that are identified in the HACCP plan.

Staff shall be trained in the work instructions relevant to their role (clause 7.1).

6.1.2   Process monitoring

Processes shall be adequately controlled and monitored to ensure that product is produced within specification. These processes may include CCPs or prerequisite programmes addressing issues such as temperature, time, pressure and chemical properties.

Monitoring shall be carried out at suitable frequencies based on experience of the reliability of equipment, frequency of process changes, and risk to product safety and quality. The frequency of checks should be included on recording forms and/or in procedure documentation.

A record of all monitoring shall be maintained.

Where processes are shown to have exceeded defined limits, corrective actions shall be taken and this action shall be recorded (clause 6.1.5).

6.1.3   In-line monitoring devices

The effective operation of equipment critical to product/process safety, legality or quality shall be ensured. Where process parameters are controlled by in-line monitoring devices (e.g. automatic temperature or pH loggers), they shall be linked to a suitable failure alert system (e.g. audible/visual alarm, machine stop function or product divert system) which is activated when defined parameters are exceeded. This alarm shall be tested routinely to ensure that it functions accurately, and records shall be maintained.

6.1.4   Critical safety or quality parameters

The objective is to ensure that products can be consistently produced and stored within the defined temperature ranges. It is recognised that process conditions are often not uniform throughout a chill store or an oven. It is important, therefore, to identify hot or cold spots, both to try to improve uniformity and to identify worst-case scenarios to ensure that all product meets at least the minimum process conditions.

The Standard expects that heat-distribution studies are carried out on cooking equipment wherever small variations in process temperature may affect the safety of the products.

Heat-distribution studies of a static oven may identify cold spots. If it is not possible to make adjustments to eliminate these cold spots, the areas should be used as the worst-case scenarios when completing heat-distribution studies.

When assessing the need to undertake temperature-distribution studies of chill or freezer facilities, the level of risk will depend on the product, the time spent in store and any margin allowed by the temperature settings (e.g. setting at -20C to ensure achievement of -18C).

Temperature-distribution studies would not normally be necessary for small chill or cold stores where product is stored only for short periods.

6.1.5   Equipment failure and results outside defined limits

In cases of equipment failure or deviation from process or specification (for example, critical limit), the company shall have defined procedures in place to ensure that the product is safe prior to its release.

As a minimum, this should include:

- identification of all products at risk, i.e. product produced since the last satisfactory check
- how the affected product will be assessed for suitability/safety (this may include sensory testing, microbiological sampling, reference to thermal process data or the use of mathematical modelling techniques, depending on the product and issue)
- who is authorised to undertake action and make a final decision on the affected product.

Records shall be kept of this deviation and the action taken.

6.1.6   Production line checks

Documented checks carried out on the production line before production commences will ensure that systems are correctly set and running. Checks shall include confirmation that:

- lines have been suitably cleaned
- lines are ready for production, with CCPs and quality parameters correctly set (for example, metal detector checks completed satisfactorily, cookers set to correct temperature programmes, correct packaging on packing line, etc.).

Checks are also required following changes of product to ensure that all product and packaging from the previous production has been removed – and, where appropriate, to ensure that cleaning has been completed correctly and the line is correctly set up for the new product.

Line checks are usually the responsibility of the line manager or supervisor. Evidence that checks have been carried out (e.g. line check sheets) and guidelines on the checks to complete should be available.

6.1.7   Packaging controls

A high proportion of product withdrawals/recalls are due to the fact that products are packed into incorrect packaging or incorrectly labelled. Therefore, specific documented packaging controls shall be in place. Particular care is required where:

- a number of similar-looking products are manufactured
- a standard product may be packed into different types of packaging
- there is a family of very similar labels for a product range, each containing different information (for example, different allergens are present or there are different use-by/best-before dates).

Procedures shall be in place to verify that adequate checks have been carried out to minimise potential errors. The frequency of checks shall be predefined, based on risk assessment, but as a minimum shall include:

- the start of packing
- during the packaging run
- following packaging or product changes
- when changing batches of packaging materials.

The procedures shall also include verification of any code information or other printing carried out at the packing stage.

6.2   Quantity – weight, volume and number control

> The company shall operate a quantity control system which conforms to legal requirements in the country where the product is sold and any additional industry sector codes or specified customer requirement.

The company shall ensure that products meet the requirements of customers and the legislation of the country, state or territory where the product is sold.

6.2.1   Quantity control – legislative requirements

The type of quantity control used (e.g. average weights, catch weight, minimum weight or count) may be determined by the company in conjunction with the requirements of the customer.

The system used shall operate to the legal requirements in the country, state or territory in which the product is sold.

Adequate records shall be kept or, where automatic check-weighing equipment is used, this shall be adequately set up and the rejection system tested according to industry-sector guidelines. Checks of automatic reject systems shall be carried out using representative packs of the product being produced.

6.2.2   Quantity control – customer requirements

Where there are no legislative requirements (e.g. where bulk quantities are supplied to the customer), procedures shall be in place to ensure that customer requirements are met (e.g. monitoring by flow meter or calibrated weighbridge for tanker loads).

Records shall be maintained.

6.3   Calibration and control of measuring and monitoring devices

The company shall be able to demonstrate that measuring and monitoring equipment is sufficiently accurate and reliable to provide confidence in measurement results.

The company shall ensure that key pieces of equipment that control and monitor processes are themselves confirmed as operating effectively and accurately. This is routinely confirmed by measurement against recognised standards. Where national or international standards do not exist, the company needs to demonstrate how the equipment is adequately monitored.

6.3.1   Identification and control of measuring equipment

The company needs to identify measuring equipment (e.g. scales, thermometers and pH meters) that is used to monitor CCPs, product safety and legality. As a minimum, this equipment must be:

- documented in a list
- marked in accordance with its calibration requirements (e.g. an identification code and the calibration due date) — this may be achieved by, for example, engraving the piece of equipment with a number that is cross-referenced to the documented list, or labelling the equipment with its calibration due date
- protected against unauthorised adjustment (e.g. through the use of programme ID codes or locking keys)
- protected from damage or misuse through design or the training of staff.

6.3.2   Calibration checks

The company needs to establish the method by which the precision and accuracy of equipment is verified. This shall include:

- a predefined check frequency, based on a risk assessment (e.g. historical reliability, nature of use, manufacturer's recommendations)
- who it shall be checked by (i.e. trained staff)
- the method to be used (which shall, where possible, be traceable to a recognised standard, e.g. use of a master calibration thermometer that has a certified test certificate traceable to a national standard).

Equipment shall be of a suitable accuracy for the measurements it is required to perform. For example, where temperature is critical to the safety of a product (e.g. pasteurisation or the canning process), the measuring thermometer requires an accuracy of +/- 0.5°C, whereas a thermometer used to check vehicle temperatures may only need an accuracy of +/- 1°C .

6.3.3   Reference equipment

All reference equipment (e.g. a master thermometer) shall be calibrated and traceable to a national or international standard.

Records shall be kept.

6.3.4   Equipment outside specified limits

Documented procedures shall detail the action to be taken when equipment is found to be outside specified limits. Documentation shall specify what will be done and by whom, and shall include what will happen to products that have been monitored by this equipment since a successful check.

Records shall be kept of the actions taken.

7 Personnel

7.1 Training

Raw material handling, preparation, processing, packing and storage areas

FUNDAMENTAL

The company shall ensure that all personnel performing work that affects product safety, legality and quality are demonstrably competent to carry out their activity, through training, work experience or qualification.

Staff shall be fully trained and competent to undertake their role. This will include all relevant staff whose roles affect product quality, legality and safety.

Seasonal/temporary personnel and contractors must be included. Where agencies are used for the provision of staff, all these requirements need to be adequately met and evidenced. This may include: specifying company policies within any supply contract; obtaining evidence of staff training records from the agency prior to a staff member commencing work; and, for example, using a risk-based system to challenge staff understanding and ensure competence in carrying out roles.

7.1.1 Initial training and supervision

The company shall ensure that all staff, including temporary staff and contractors, receive training to a level commensurate with their responsibility and the type of work they carry out. The following may be considered:

- induction training for all staff, covering company policies on hygiene, allergens, quality requirements, etc.
- qualification in 'basic food hygiene' for food handlers
- training in areas that impact food safety, such as cleaning, machine operation, quality inspections and sampling.

All personnel shall be adequately supervised throughout the working period. Particular attention should be paid to identifying the needs of temporary/seasonal workers and contractors.

7.1.2 Critical control point training

To ensure that activities identified as CCPs within the HACCP food safety plan are managed correctly, personnel involved in these areas shall be appropriately trained in the procedure. This includes the operation of the control, monitoring activities and corrective action. Clear, documented instructions shall be available, detailing:

- how to carry out the tasks
- when the task is to be completed
- records to be maintained
- action to be taken in the event of a non-conforming result.

A competency assessment shall take place on completion of training and at predefined intervals – for example, during CCP internal audits. The assessment needs to confirm that the procedure is followed correctly, test knowledge of corrective actions and check completion of relevant training.

7.1.3   Documented training programme

The company shall have a documented training programme showing that job role competencies are identified, actions are undertaken to ensure that staff obtain these competencies, and a review of the effectiveness of these actions is undertaken. For example, a job training matrix could be used to list all of the site roles and details of which procedures and work instructions are required for each role.

Training shall be delivered in an appropriate language for the trainee (for example, by providing either written or oral translation where it is required). It is not a requirement for all documentation to be translated into every language of the workforce, but it is a requirement that all staff can understand the instructions necessary for their job. For example, hygiene rules may be provided in written translations or in pictorial format, and CCP monitoring instructions may be translated into languages spoken by staff involved in these areas.

Training may be delivered internally or externally, but the company needs to ensure that the training has been effective – for example, through assessment of the staff's ability to undertake the tasks they need to perform.

7.1.4   Training records

Evidence of all training needs to be kept and must include:

- the name of the trainee and confirmation of attendance
- the date and duration of training
- the course title or contents
- the name of the training provider.

This information may all be included in the certificate of attendance provided at an external or internal course, or the course contents (e.g. personnel induction booklet) kept and cross-referenced with a record of training (with trainee name, date and name of trainer, together with the name of any translator).

Remember to ensure that training records for any temporary staff, agency-supplied labour or external consultants are also available.

7.1.5   Competency review

The company shall ensure there is ongoing assessment of staff competency in their roles (e.g. through one-to-one appraisals, team performance monitoring by line managers, review of the results of internal audits, or review of records).

Where the need is identified, there shall be appropriate refresher training, coaching, mentoring or on-the-job experience to improve skills and understanding.

7.2   Personal hygiene

Raw materials handling, preparation, processing, packing and storage areas

The company's personal hygiene standards shall be appropriate to the products produced, documented, and adopted by all personnel, including agency staff, contractors and visitors to the production facility.

All personnel entering production areas (including raw material storage, processing, packing and storage areas) shall adhere to the company's documented personal hygiene rules. These should be based on risk and may take into account different requirements for different product risk zones.

7.2.1   Documented personal hygiene policy

The company shall document its personal hygiene requirements. As a minimum, these will include the following:

- Jewellery shall not be worn. Exceptions shall be minimal and shall not constitute a risk to product (e.g. wrist bands identifying a particular medical condition may be worn where product is not at risk of contamination). Only plain wedding bands/wrist bands (i.e. without any stones that may fall out) are permitted.

- The Standard clearly states that rings and studs in exposed parts of the body such as ears, noses, tongues and eyebrows shall not be worn.

- Watches are not permitted in open product areas.

- Long fingernails are a contamination hazard since they may break off, and hence are not permitted; nor are nail varnish or false nails. Fingernails shall be kept clean, commensurate with the level of hygiene expected within a food manufacturing environment. Where visitors cannot comply with these rules, other controls (such as limiting where visitors may enter and what they may touch, and the obligatory use of gloves) shall be implemented to minimise the risk of contamination.

- Excessive perfume or aftershave shall not be worn as this has the potential to taint foods.

These requirements are applicable to raw material handling, preparation, processing, packing and storage areas. The requirements for staff working solely in enclosed product areas may be relaxed where no risk is presented to the products.

The requirements shall be communicated to all personnel (e.g. through induction training records for all staff and sign-in procedures for visitors and contractors). Consideration shall be given to staff who are non-native speakers and appropriate methods of training (e.g. use of translators) shall be provided for them.

Compliance with requirements shall be checked regularly – for example, by incorporating checks into daily/weekly GMP audits, or through challenge/questioning of personnel at regular intervals.

7.2.2   Hand cleaning

Hand cleaning shall be conducted at a frequency appropriate to the level of risk to the product being produced and in line with good industry practice. As a minimum, hands shall be washed before entering production and after going to the toilet, eating, smoking or blowing noses.

Appropriate instructions for hand washing, considering the language needs of staff (e.g. including pictorial instructions), shall be provided (clause 4.8.6).

7.2.3   Cuts and grazes

Cuts and grazes on exposed areas of skin shall be covered to prevent contamination of product.

To minimise the potential for plasters to contaminate product, they shall be controlled by the company – for instance, through the use of an issue procedure (e.g. numbering the plasters and documenting in a log when and to whom they were issued). The company may consider the need for an audit at the end of the shift and/or for staff to immediately inform supervisors of any loss of plasters.

Plasters shall be visually distinct (preferably blue) and include a metal-detectable strip.

Where appropriate, in addition to the plaster, a glove shall be worn.

7.2.4   Metal detectable plasters

To ensure that each batch of plasters purchased fulfils the metal-detectable requirement, a sample from each batch shall be tested to confirm that it is successfully rejected by the metal detector or X-ray equipment in use. Records shall be kept.

Where the site does not use metal detectors, this requirement will not apply.

7.2.5   Personal medicines

Personal medicines need to be controlled to ensure they do not constitute a risk to product. The site shall have a documented procedure.

Wherever possible, medicines will not be taken into production areas. However, where staff have a medical need to keep personal medicines with them (e.g. they are asthmatics or diabetics), procedures shall be in place to control these medicines (e.g. a requirement to notify the company of the defined medical need).

7.3 Medical screening

The company shall ensure that procedures are in place to ensure that employees, agency staff, contractors or visitors are not a source of transmission of food-borne diseases to products.

7.3.1 Illness notification procedures

Personnel need to receive, as part of their training, clear instructions on the potential risks of food-borne disease and the company's procedures for notification where the employee may be suffering from a condition which may place products at risk.

The company shall be expected to define the infections of concern, as advised by local legislation (e.g. list of communicable diseases).

These policies shall be documented.

The company may consider use of a pre-employment and/or return-to-work medical questionnaire or medical examination (e.g. stool testing), as appropriate to the risk.

The use of suitably trained and competent persons and the use of external medical experts may be required, particularly where privacy laws exist.

7.3.2 Medical questionnaire for site visitors

The company shall ensure that visitors and contractors who enter areas where there may be a risk to product safety, or who undertake work that may constitute a risk to product, are suitably medically screened by use of a questionnaire. The company shall ensure that regular visitors and contractors, such as external company staff or pest control providers, are included.

Where questionnaires are used, these shall be reviewed by a competent person.

The procedure shall be documented.

7.3.3 Documented infectious disease procedure

Where staff, visitors or contractors declare they are suffering from, or have been in contact with, the identified diseases, infections, etc., they shall be subject to, and informed of, the procedures to prevent product contamination. This will usually include relocation to a role where they are not in contact with open products.

7.4 Protective clothing

Employees or visitors to production areas

Suitable company-issued protective clothing shall be worn by employees, contractors or visitors working in or entering production areas.

Protective clothing includes uniforms, overalls, head coverings (such as hats and hairnets), shoes and boots, aprons and gloves (whether disposable or washable). A suitable design shall be provided to employees, visitors and contractors by the company.

7.4.1   Documented protective clothing policy

The company is required to determine the procedures for application and use of protective clothing, based on a risk assessment. The risk assessment shall consider foreign-body, microbiological and allergen risks as appropriate, as well as general good practice principles. It shall document:

- what shall be worn
- where and how clothing shall be put on and taken off
- where it shall be stored
- special requirements for specific areas (e.g. high-risk and high-care areas require dedicated protective clothing that is not worn in other areas of the site – see clause 7.4.4)
- removal of protective clothing before entering toilets
- procedures for canteens and smoking areas
- areas where the product is fully enclosed and has no or very little risk of contamination from the factory environment during normal production.

The requirement to wear full company-issued protective clothing would not be an absolute requirement where *all* of the following criteria apply:

- all products are fully enclosed
- the product would, if it were not fully enclosed, be classed as a low-risk product
- the area is separate from areas containing open product
- staff do not need to pass through open product areas to access the area.

The wearing of a company uniform is preferred. Where personal clothing is allowed, sites must provide guidance on the standards of clothing which will be acceptable.

Wherever product lines are entered (for instance, adjustments at the filler), protective clothing and hair coverings must be worn.

7.4.2   Design of protective clothing

The company needs to consider the design of protective clothing and ensure that it is suitable for the production processes. As a minimum:

- The clothing shall not include external pockets above the waist (e.g. no pockets in coats) and shall not have sewn-on buttons.
- The company shall consider the design of protective footwear for production areas and shall provide footwear that can be kept clean.
- Headwear such as mob hats or hairnets shall ensure that head hair is completely covered to minimise potential contamination.
- Snoods shall be provided for staff or visitors who have beards or moustaches, where protection is needed to prevent product contamination. Clear rules shall be in place and understood by staff, based on clear assessment by the company.

Clothing shall be available for all staff and items shall be provided in sufficient numbers that they may be maintained in an acceptable condition during working (e.g. to allow for washing).

7.4.3   Laundry

Protective clothing may be cleaned by contracting the services of a specialised laundry, by laundering in-house or, in exceptional circumstances, by laundering by employees.

External contracted services shall be incorporated within the company's purchasing supplier approval programme (clause 3.5.3) and have systems of approval and continual assessment to ensure that the process is under control. This should be based on risk assessment and may include self-audit questionnaires where low-risk products are manufactured. The monitoring of the effectiveness of cleaning is likely to consist of visual assessment and the monitoring of complaints.

In-house laundering carried out on the company premises shall be controlled. This is likely to be via HACCP-style principles, controls and validation data, such as monitoring of the temperature and detergent, specifying items not to be washed together, overseeing drying processes and visual inspection.

Home laundering may be deemed acceptable in low-risk operations such as produce packing or enclosed process areas where the clothing is worn primarily to protect the worker from the product (for instance, raw root vegetables). This needs to be controlled by written instructions to staff, to include how garments are to be washed (temperature, detergent, specifying items not to be washed together and drying instructions). Employees shall be provided with a suitable means to safely transport washed garments from home to the workplace (sealable plastic bags or similar). There shall be a defined responsibility within the company for monitoring the effectiveness of the system. This is typically achieved by visual inspection. There shall also be a procedure and system for effectively dealing with any case where employees are unable to perform self-laundry, either through lack of diligence or through lack of facilities. This system shall be capable of being brought into immediate effect once a problem has been identified.

Home laundering still requires appropriate care and attention to ensure that potential pathogens on clothes worn for work are removed or killed. For example, clothes worn for work should be washed separately from other laundry in an automatic washing machine using the hottest temperature the material of the clothes will withstand and the 'full load' setting. When thoroughly dried, the clothes should be ironed with a hot iron to further heat-disinfect the clothes.

7.4.4   Protective clothing for high-care or high-risk areas

The company will need to assess and monitor the laundry (e.g. through visual inspection, regular audits and a complaints procedure) to ensure that the process is maintained and under control.

The laundry must be able to demonstrate that it has processes to ensure:

- a suitable level of cleanliness – for example, microbiological validation and verification tests have been completed

- clothes are commercially sterile – 'commercially sterile' means the removal of vegetative forms of micro-organisms associated with food poisoning and/or spoilage (to achieve this, a garment should be processed at a temperature no lower than 65°C for a minimum of 10 minutes, or processed at a temperature no lower than 71°C for a minimum of 3 minutes)

- adequate segregation between dirty and cleaned clothes

- protection of cleaned clothes from contamination until delivered to the site (e.g. through the use of covers or bags).

7.4.5   Gloves

Gloves are a potential source of foreign bodies. Therefore, sufficient control procedures (such as regular inspection and replacement) need to be put in place to ensure they are intact and do not shed loose fibres. The company needs to consider the design of gloves used and whether they need to be disposable, of food grade and of a visually distinct colour from the product (preferably blue).

7.4.6   Protective clothing that cannot be laundered

A documented procedure shall be developed for protective items that cannot be laundered – for example, shoes, chain mail, gloves and aprons.

The frequency of cleaning and sanitisation shall be based on risk.

SECTION III

FOLLOWING THE AUDIT

Section III

Following the Audit

1   The Closing Meeting

At the closing meeting, the non-conformities identified will be discussed between the company and the auditor. (Explanations of the levels of non-conformity and their consequences are given in sections 9 and 10 in Part 1 of the Audit Protocol in the Standard.) However, it should be noted that these comments are provisional and hence the auditor cannot give a conclusion as to the audit grade. This is because all the evidence of the audit, including the report and the non-conformities, is reviewed independently by member(s) of the Certification Body to ensure consistency. Although it does not occur frequently, the level of non-conformity identified may be changed and this may affect the final grade.

Where the combination of non-conformities identified results in the awarding of no grade, no certificate is issued. Where this is the site's first audit against Issue 6 of the Standard, the site will automatically be transferred into the Enrolment Programme (see section 4 in Part 2 of the Audit Protocol in the Standard). Sites which have previously been certificated to Issue 6 of the Standard are not eligible for the Enrolment Programme and therefore a further full audit will be required, which will include verification that appropriate corrective action has taken place to close out the non-conformities. The company will choose when this subsequent audit takes place, depending on the action that needs to be taken to rectify the identified issues. It should be noted, however, that where certification is withdrawn, the company must inform its customers of its uncertificated status, together with the proposed corrective action plan.

A written summary of the non-conformities will be left with the company at the closing meeting or within one day of the closing meeting. If the company is unclear about any of the non-conformities or the expected action required to correct the non-conformities, they should talk with their Certification Body as soon as possible.

At the closing meeting, the auditor will also explain that all of the audit data will be uploaded into the BRC Directory (www.brcdirectory.com) and that the company can view the information.

2   Handling Non-conformities and Corrective Action and Root Cause Analysis

The auditor will identify issues and document these as non-conformities. It is a feature of BRC certification that all non-conformities need to be corrected before a certificate can be issued. Evidence must be provided to demonstrate that corrective action has been effected, and the company has 28 calendar days to supply this evidence.

The Certification Body has to satisfy itself with the evidence provided, and therefore has the option to revisit the site to view the action taken or accept the submission of documentary evidence. This will be indicated to the company prior to the submission of evidence. However, where the total number of non-conformities results in the site being awarded a grade C, a revisit will *always* be required to close non-conformities.

It is at the discretion of the Certification Body whether a revisit is carried out. However, a revisit may be favoured where:

- there are a relatively large number of minor non-conformities
- documentary evidence of compliance would be difficult to demonstrate effectively, **e.g.** where there are several incidents of poor cleaning
- there is a history of non-conformities closed through documentary evidence, recurring at subsequent audits.

2.1   Revisits

Where revisits are required, these shall be scheduled to occur within the 28-day window allowed for the closure of non-conformities for certified sites. Revisits should ideally be undertaken by the original auditor, but this may not be possible.

The revisit shall focus on establishing that the original non-conformities have been corrected effectively. However, at any stage of the audit process, further non-conformities may be identified that need to be satisfactorily actioned before certification is awarded (although they will not influence the grade awarded).

2.2   Documentary evidence

Where a revisit is not required, satisfactory documentary evidence must be provided to demonstrate that the non-conformities identified at the audit have been corrected. It is important that the evidence provided clearly demonstrates compliance.

Documentary evidence is usually in the following formats:

- Procedures – where evidence is in the form of a new or changed procedure, supplementary evidence to show that the changes have been put into operation may also be required (e.g. training record/recording form).

- Records – where new forms or recording sheets have been introduced to correct an issue, the submitted evidence must include a completed record to show that these are in use. A training record may also be required. The site shall ensure that these records are completed correctly. Ideally, a series of completed records (e.g. over several consecutive days) shall be included.

- Photographic evidence – photographs should ideally be taken before and after corrective action to demonstrate the change. Photographs need to show clearly that the particular non-conformity has been corrected. For instance, it may be necessary to have a series of photographs zooming in on a particular piece of equipment that has been modified or cleaned to enable the auditor to identify that it is the correct item.

- Invoices/receipts – invoices or receipts for new equipment shall be sufficiently detailed to demonstrate that the non-conformity has been addressed.

See Appendix 4 for an example of documentary evidence to correct a specified non-conformity.

2.3   Root cause analysis

Root cause analysis is the process of conducting an investigation into an identified problem, to allow the investigator(s) to understand the fundamental or underlying cause of the non-conformity and implement suitable action preventing recurrence of the same issue. It is a completely separate process from the immediate corrective action described earlier in this section.

Following the audit, the root cause of all of the non-conformities identified by the auditor must be identified and an action plan, complete with timescales, submitted to the Certification Body within 28 days. (It should be noted that, because the action plan must be submitted within 28 days, the root cause analysis must be completed within this timescale. However, a longer timescale may be required to effectively implement all of the root-cause actions.)

There is no prescribed method of conducting a root cause analysis, but clause 3.7.1 of this Guideline highlights one suitable method (the 'Five Whys' technique).

Example 1

Non-conformity: Internal audit of the supplier-management systems scheduled for January had not been carried out.

Corrective action taken: Audit completed. All scheduled audits completed and up to date.

Evidence submitted: Copy of audit reports.

Root cause analysis: The analysis quickly establishes the cause – insufficient staff due to sickness. However, this is not a failure of a system or process and is, therefore, unlikely to be manageable. Further investigation is thus required – for example, to establish why another employee didn't complete the audit. The answer may be that the procedures didn't incorporate the need for deputies and, therefore, no alternative staff had the appropriate qualifications or training.

Proposed action plan:

- Update internal audit process/policy to incorporate deputies.

- Identify suitable deputies or increase the size of the internal audit team.

- Ensure that suitable training is completed.

Example 2

Non-conformity: Duration of training is not recorded on staff training records.

Corrective action taken: Training records updated.

Evidence submitted: Copies of updated records.

Root cause analysis: The staff responsible for completing the training records were not aware of this requirement because there was no space for recording times on the training record form. This was because training times are not mentioned in the training procedure.

Proposed action plan:

- Training procedure updated to reflect current requirements.

- New training record form introduced with provision for time to be recorded.

- The staff responsible for completing the training form are trained in the new procedure.

2.4   Timing

In order to achieve or maintain certification, the company must have understood the requirements of the Standard and have well-established systems and processes. It is, therefore, expected that sites that can be certificated will not have significant issues identified at the audit that will take a long time to solve. Accordingly, 28 days are allowed for either the submission of documentary evidence or a revisit to demonstrate compliance. Where the evidence provided is inconclusive, a period of 2–3 days may be accepted to provide additional information. However, this would normally be included within the 28-day period (i.e. the company should submit the evidence sufficiently in advance of the deadline). Where satisfactory evidence of corrective action or a root-cause action plan is not provided within this timescale, certification may not be granted.

3   The Audit Report

The report produced as a result of the audit is one of the key outputs from the process and is used to provide information about the company's site for its customers. This reduces the need for customers' own audits, and companies are encouraged to share details of the audit reports with customers and potential customers.

3.1   The report format

The BRC has a set format for the reporting of audits to ensure that consistent information is provided, and to make it easier for users of reports to find information within the report. Reports shall be provided in a typed format.

The report is in several sections:

- Audit summary – details of the company, scope of audit, etc.

- Results – certification status, grade, summary of the non-conformities.

- Company details – address, technical contacts, etc.

- Company profile – size of company, type of business, other certifications, etc.

- Product characteristics – product categories, product safety rationale, etc.

- Audit duration details – times and dates of the audit.

- Key personnel – including those present during the audit.

- Non-conformity summary sheets – giving details of the non-conformities identified, the action taken and the root cause analysis.

- Detailed audit report – giving detailed information to allow any reader to understand the control processes in place and what evidence was seen during the audit.

3.2   Report ownership

Audit reports remain the property of the company commissioning the audit and shall not be released in whole or in part to a third party unless prior consent has been given. Companies are encouraged, however, to release the report to customers.

4   Certification

Once all documentation has been reviewed by the Certification Body, the certificate shall be issued in the specified format. Note that the certificate remains the property of the Certification Body.

The Certification Body may carry out further visits or question activities to validate continued certification at any time, whether announced or unannounced. For example, this may be due to a product recall or information from another source, such as a customer contacting the BRC. The aim is to safeguard certification, ensuring that it is operated by the company as a year-round scheme.

The company must ensure that ongoing certification is maintained. Under no circumstances can the validity of a certificate be extended. The company should liaise with customers if it finds itself out of certification for any reason.

5   Use of Logo

The BRC certificated company logo can be used by companies that have achieved certification against the Standard (it is not available to companies in the Enrolment Programme) and that have agreed with the guidelines for use.

The logo can be used on all company communication tools, such as vehicles, letterheads, compliment slips, business cards, marketing collateral, advertising, exhibition graphics and electronic media, subject to the terms of usage (such as use in specified sizes and colours). It may not be used on product packaging.

6   The Directory

The publicly accessible section of the BRC Directory (www.brcdirectory.com) lists all of the companies that have achieved BRC certification and are 'officially' recognised. It is, therefore, a central point to confirm the validity of a company's certification. The Directory also lists BRC-approved Certification Bodies. This helps to ensure consistency throughout the certification process and adherence to BRC requirements.

The second section of the BRC Directory is password protected (i.e. not publicly accessible). It contains the site's audit report. This section of the Directory also enables sites to share their reports with their customers.

APPENDICES

Appendix 1

Guidelines on Defining Production Risk Zones

The Standard identifies four different risk zones within the processing and storage facilities, with corresponding levels of hygiene requirements and segregation to reduce the potential for product contamination. The decision tree (Figure 2) provides a guide to defining the risk zones classified as:

- Enclosed product area
- Low risk – open product area
- High care – open product area
- High risk – open product area.

The food safety controls operated within the factory areas shall be appropriate for the risks to the product. The expectations for factory hygiene, finish of the buildings, equipment and protective clothing/staff hygiene should reflect the potential risks to the product. Identifying areas of different risk helps to ensure appropriate food safety controls are in place and identify the need to restrict the movement of personnel and materials between areas.

1   Enclosed Product Area

An enclosed product area is defined as an area of the factory where all of the products are fully enclosed and therefore not vulnerable to environmental contamination (e.g. by foreign bodies or micro-organisms).

This includes areas where:

- the product is fully enclosed within packaging, e.g. raw material and finished product storage and dispatch areas
- the product is fully enclosed within equipment shielding the product from physical or microbiological contamination from the production environment during production. This may include enclosure within transfer pipework and fully enclosed equipment, and also where the equipment maintains its own environment to protect the product, e.g. aseptic filling equipment.

Areas meeting these criteria are typically found in liquid processing plants (e.g. dairies, wineries, and soft drinks or water bottling factories) and some highly mechanised industries such as flour mills, sugar refining and oil processing facilities.

2   Open Product Areas

Wherever ingredients, intermediate or finished products are not protected from the factory environment there is a potential risk of product contamination by foreign bodies, allergenic material or micro-organisms in the environment.

The significance of the risk of microbiological contamination will depend upon the susceptibility of the product to support the growth or survival of pathogens and the expected storage conditions, shelf life and further treatment of the product at the factory or by the consumer.

In determining the zones particular consideration shall be given to the risks presented by pathogens such as *Listeria*). It should be recognised that some products considered as low risk on this basis will nevertheless require high standards of microbiological control, similar to a high-care area, because spoilage organisms present a significant risk (e.g. yeasts in yogurt, mould on hard cheese).

2.1   Low risk

In this area the greatest risk can be considered as physical contamination. The significance to human health of microbiological contamination is reduced because the product is unsuitable for the growth of pathogens or is designed to undergo a later validated kill step that ensures the product is safe to eat. Consideration does, however, need to be given to the risk of pre-process spoilage and of contamination by pathogens which may survive but not grow on products (e.g. *Salmonella* on chocolate, peanut butter or dried milk powder).

The hygiene standards in such areas generally require greater emphasis on preventing foreign body and allergen contamination of products.

These areas include:

- the production of products which will *always* require cooking before consumption e.g. raw meats, prepared meals and pizzas with uncooked components and where instructions require products are to be fully cooked* before eating

- production facilities where products are either processed within the final container or are unsuitable for the growth of pathogens and therefore stored and distributed as ambient products, e.g. canned products, pH-controlled products such as pickles, low a_w foods such as dried foods and confectionery, and some baked products

- production facilities where ready-to-eat products are stored chilled to preserve the quality of the product but which have other controls to prevent the growth of pathogens, e.g. hard cheese

- production areas where processes are undertaken prior to the introduction of a validated kill step in the process, such as cooking, e.g. mixing and preparation areas prior to cooking.

2.2   High care

This is an area designed to a high standard where practices relating to personnel, ingredients, equipment, packaging and environment aim to *minimise* product contamination by pathogenic micro-organisms. Segregation of the high-care area and access arrangements to the area shall minimise the risk of product contamination.

Products requiring handling in a high-care area have all of the following characteristics:

- potentially vulnerable to the growth of pathogens

- all microbiologically susceptible components have received a process to reduce the microbiological contamination to safe levels (typically 1–2 log reduction of micro-organisms) before entry to the area

- the finished products are ready to eat or heat** or, on the basis of known consumer use, are likely to be eaten without adequate cooking (see HACCP 2.3.1)

- the finished products require chilling or freezing during storage.

Although all vulnerable products have, before entry to the high-care area, received a process to reduce pathogenic bacteria to a level to make the products safe to eat, spoilage organisms will be present and shall be controlled by temperature and shelf life. Examples of products produced in such an area include sandwiches, ready prepared salads, unpasteurised soft cheeses, fermented and dried meats, cold smoked salmon, prepared meals designed to be reheated only and some chilled pizzas.

Products produced in high-care areas may themselves present hazards to other products; for instance the use of salad products, even when processed by rinsing in chlorine solution to reduce microbial load, may still present an increased risk of *Listeria*, and this needs to be taken into account when planning hygiene regimes and production planning within the high-care area.

Where a customer specifically requires their products to be produced in a high-care area, this shall not compromise the safety of other products produced in the same high-care area.

2.3   High risk

This is a physically segregated area, designed to a high standard of hygiene where practices relating to personnel, ingredients, equipment packaging and environment aim to *prevent* contamination by pathogenic micro-organisms.

Products requiring handling in a high-risk area have all of the following characteristics:

◼   potentially vulnerable to the growth of pathogens, particularly *Listeria*

◼   all components have received a full cook process, minimum 70°C for 2 minutes or equivalent before entry to the area

◼   the finished products are ready to eat or heat** or, on the basis of known consumer use, are likely to be eaten without adequate cooking (see HACCP 2.3.1)

◼   the finished products require chilling or freezing during storage.

Products considered as high risk include cooked sliced meats, fully cooked prepared meals and dairy desserts.

Where products are designed such that they meet the requirements for a re-heat product (i.e. all components receive a full cook of 70°C for 2 minutes but also have full cooking instructions), these should be considered for production in high-risk areas.

Specific high-care and high-risk requirements

The requirements relating to processing environment and general GMPs within the Standard are always expected to be adopted in relation to product risk. There are, however, some clauses within the Standard which identify particular and specific requirements applying to high-care or high-risk areas to ensure a consistent expectation. In such clauses the words High care and High risk will appear in bold type. These clauses are 4.3.1, 4.3.5, 4.3.6, 4.4.4, 4.4.13, 4.8.4, 4.8.5 and 4.11.5.

The presence of high-care and high-risk areas and the controls in place at the site shall be included on the audit report.

Definitions

*Cook – is a thermal process undertaken by the user of the product which is designed to achieve typically a 6 log reduction in *Listeria monocytogenes* equivalent to 70°C for 2 minutes. Alternative cooking processes may be accepted where these meet recognised national guidelines and are validated by scientific data.

**Reheat – products that are designed to be safe to be consumed without the need for a full cook; the reheating of the product is intended to make the product more palatable and is not a microbiological kill step.

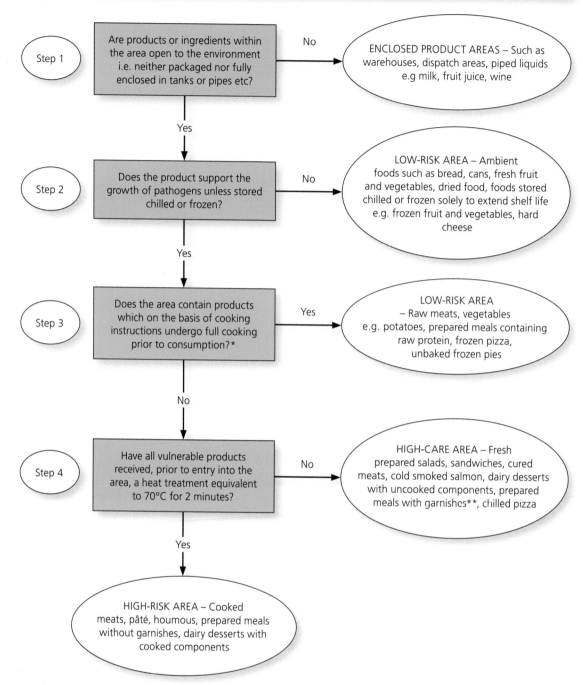

* Thermal treatment equivalent to 70°C for 2 minutes.
** Raw or not pH/a_w stabilised so will support the growth of *L.monocytogenes*.

Figure 2 Production zone decision tree

This decision tree provides a guide only to the categorisation of production zones and cannot take account of specific product characteristics (e.g. pH, a_w) or the vulnerability of particular products to pathogens or spoilage which may result in exceptions. A detailed risk assessment should be undertaken where necessary to support the decision. Reference shall be made to the more detailed explanations of product zones in the guideline.

Appendix 2

Codex Alimentarius Four-step Decision Tree

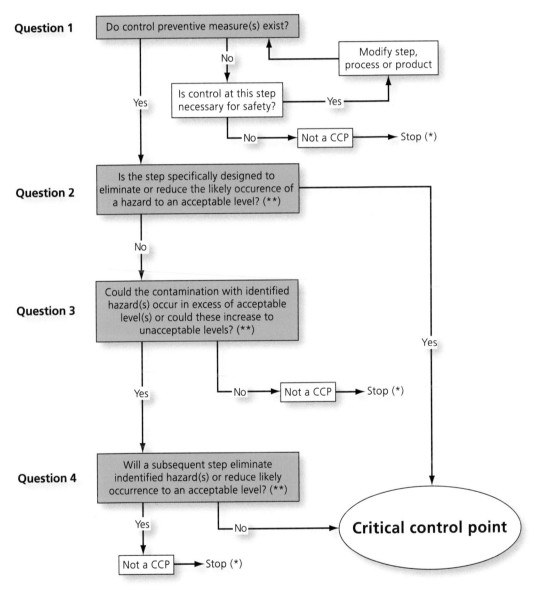

Example of decision tree to identify critical control points (CCPs)

Answer questions in sequence

Question 1 — Do control preventive measure(s) exist?

No → Is control at this step necessary for safety? → Yes → Modify step, process or product

Yes ↓

Is control at this step necessary for safety? → No → Not a CCP → Stop (*)

Question 2 — Is the step specifically designed to eliminate or reduce the likely occurence of a hazard to an acceptable level? (**)

No ↓

Question 3 — Could the contamination with identified hazard(s) occur in excess of acceptable level(s) or could these increase to unacceptable levels? (**)

Yes ↓   No → Not a CCP → Stop (*)

Yes → (from Question 2)

Question 4 — Will a subsequent step eliminate indentified hazard(s) or reduce likely occurrence to an acceptable level? (**)

Yes ↓   No → Critical control point

Not a CCP → Stop (*)

* Proceed to the next identified hazard in the described process.

** Acceptable and unacceptable levels need to be defined within the overall objectives in identifying the CCPs of the HACCP plan.

Appendix 3

Example of a Risk Assessment

The Standard requires that documented glass, brittle and hard plastic, ceramics and other materials are checked at a frequency based on risk assessment.

The company has identified the items to be monitored and has developed a check frequency based on a risk rating for the potential of broken glass to contaminate product, either directly or via personnel.

Item	Location	Hazard	Risk rating	Audit frequency
Pressure-gauge casing (glass) on packing machine	Packing area	Glass entering (open) product directly	High	Line start-up checks every shift
Inspection window (reinforced glass) from high-risk to low-risk area	Packing area	Glass entering (open) product directly or contaminating production area	High	Daily area checks
Lights (protected glass)	Raw material storage area	Glass entering raw materials (sealed) or contaminating protective clothing	High	Daily area checks
Lights (protected glass)	Dispatch area	Glass entering finished product (sealed) or contaminating protective clothing	Medium	Weekly area checks
Lights (protected glass)	Administration offices	Glass contaminating clothing. Change procedure before entering production areas	Low	Monthly area checks

Appendix 4

Example of Documented Evidence Submitted for Corrective Action and Root Cause Analysis

No.	Requirement ref.	Details of non-conformity	Corrective action taken	Root cause analysis and proposed action plan	Evidence provided (document/ photograph/ visit/other)	Reviewed by and date reviewed
Major non-conformity						
1	4.10.3.6	Metal detectors on both roll plants failed to reject ferrous and non-ferrous test pieces (synchronisation error).	Engineer called and adjusted synchronisation immediately. Test method changed to include rejection of test packs. Staff trained.	Root cause analysis: 1) Not reported by staff. 2) No periodic countersigning of metal detector checks by line manager (e.g. at end of production run or end of shift). 3) Internal audits did not identify the fault. (N.B. this implies another issue that requires further investigation.) Proposed action plan: 1) Staff retrained in the importance of, and requirements for, metal detection. (This is not the same as the procedure training listed in corrective action.) 2) Specific checks on all metal detectors included in the internal audit schedule. 3) Review of all items in the internal audit programme to ensure all the relevant systems and processes have been included. 4) Metal detection procedure and record sheets updated to include requirement for sign-off by a suitable manager (e.g. a shift or line manager).	Copy procedure and training record.	M Oliver 26/07/2012

Appendix 5

Example of a Documented Procedure and Record

Excellent Foods		Sanitiser V100 Concentration Check Record	EF 001

1. Introduction

To ensure that sanitiser solutions are made to the correct concentration (target 0.9–1.25%). To ensure effective use, random daily checks shall be made.

2. Responsibility

The Cleaning Team Supervisor shall ensure their team is appropriately trained to carry out this procedure as specified.

3. Area

High-care areas 1 and 2.

4. Check frequency

Daily – as a minimum, three samples at the start of each shift, for each area.

5. Record

To be documented on record RE 001 and checked by Shift Manager before transfer to technical department.

6. Equipment required

Safety equipment – gloves and safety glasses

Test equipment – plastic syringe, plastic flask (approximately 100 ml)

Test solutions – phenolphthalein, 1M sodium hydroxide.

7. Test procedure for Sanitiser V100

7.1 Wearing gloves and safety glasses, use the syringe to take a 40 ml sample from the sample point.

7.2 Rinse out plastic flask with approximately 10 ml of sample from the syringe and discard this solution.

7.3 Add 20 ml of the sample solution to the flask.

7.4 Add three drops of phenolphthalein indicator. Swirl gently; the solution will remain colourless.

7.5 Add the 1M sodium hydroxide solution **(safety – ensure that gloves and glasses are worn)** drop by drop until the colour changes to the first permanent pink. Count and record the number of drops on record RE 001.

8. Target values

Target value is 5 to 7 drops.

9. Corrective action

9.1 Report where the drops are below or above the target, i.e. <5 or >7.

9.2 Discard the sanitiser solution and refill with new batch using doser. Retest this solution.

9.3 Record the action taken on record RE 001.

Version 1	Date: 1.1.12	Page 1 of 2	Approved by Technical Manager	Sanitiser Check Method

Excellent Foods		Sanitiser V100 Concentration Check Record	RE 001

Three sampled points at the start of each shift for high-care areas 1 and 2 to be completed by cleaning teams.

Summary procedure (ref EF 001) for Sanitiser V100

- Wearing gloves and safety glasses, use the syringe to take a 40 ml sample from the sample point.
- Rinse out plastic flask with approximately 10 ml of sample from the syringe and discard this solution.
- Add 20 ml of the sample solution to the flask.
- Add three drops of phenolphthalein indicator. Swirl gently; the solution will remain colourless.
- Add the 1M sodium hydroxide solution **(safety – ensure that gloves and glasses are worn)** drop by drop until the colour changes to pink. Count and record the number of drops on record RE 001.

Corrective action

Report to Shift Manager when outside **target of 5 to 7 drops**. Discard the sanitiser solution and refill with new batch using doser. Retest this solution.

DATE: _____/_____/_____   AREA: _____   SHIFT: _____

Time	Sample description	Number of drops	Signed	Corrective action	Signed

Checked and signed by Shift Manager: Date:

Version 1	Date: 1.1.12	Page 2 of 2	Approved by Technical Manager	Sanitiser Check Method

© BRC   117

Appendix 6

Equivalent Processes to Achieve 70°C for 2 Minutes Calculated Using a z Value of 7.5°C

Temperature at the slowest heating point	Lethal rate (equivalent minutes to 1 minute at 70°C)	Number of minutes required at the reference temperature to achieve an equivalent process
60	0.046	43.48
61	0.063	31.74
62	0.086	23.26
63	0.116	17.24
64	0.158	12.66
65	0.215	9.30
66	0.293	6.83
67	0.398	5.02
68	0.541	3.70
69	0.735	2.72
70	1.00	2.00
71	1.36	1.47
72	1.85	1.08
73	2.51	0.80 (48 seconds)
74	3.41	0.60 (36 seconds)
75	4.64	0.43 (26 seconds)
76	6.31	0.32 (19 seconds)
77	8.58	0.23 (14 seconds)
78	11.66	0.17 (10 seconds)
79	15.85	0.13 (8 seconds)
80	21.54	0.09 (5 seconds)

For example, if heating at 68°C, it can be seen from the above table that 1 minute of heating at 68°C is equivalent to 0.541 minutes at 70°C. Therefore, to achieve the equivalent of 2 minutes at 70°C, it would be necessary to heat at 68°C for 3.70 minutes (2÷0.541=3.70).

This table is reproduced with permission from Campden BRI Guideline 51 – *Pasteurisation: A Food Industry Practical Guide (Second edition)*. It is for illustrative purposes only. The equivalent times given are dependent on the z value of the organism in question, which in this example is given as 7.5°C. Z values vary from one strain to another, and can also change with temperature. Copies of the document are available from the Campden BRI publications section (telephone: +44 (0)1386 842048, email: pubs@campden.co.uk).

Sources of Further Information

BRC Global Standards

A series of globally recognised certification standards for manufacturers and for storage and distribution companies.

www.brcglobalstandards.com

BRC Guidelines

A series of best-practice guidelines on topics including complaint handling, pest control, internal auditing, product recall, traceability and foreign-body detection.

www.brcbookshop.com

Codex Alimentarius

The Codex Alimentarius Commission was created in 1963 by FAO and WHO to develop food standards, guidelines and related texts such as codes of practice under the Joint FAO/WHO Food Standards Programme.

The downloadable *Food Hygiene – Basic Texts 2003* includes HACCP steps.

www.codexalimentarius.net

Food and Drug Administration (FDA) of the United States 'Bad Bug Book'

Examples of microbiological sources.

http://www.fda.gov/Food/FoodSafety/FoodborneIllness/
FoodborneIllnessFoodbornePathogensNaturalToxins/BadBugBook/default.htm

RASFF

The Rapid Alert System for Food and Feed (RASFF), established in 1979, enables the rapid exchange of information whenever a risk to food or feed safety is identified. Members comprise 27 member states, the European Commission, the European Food Safety Authority, Iceland, Liechtenstein and Norway. This is part of the Europa website.

http://ec.europa.eu/food/food/rapidalert/index_en.htm

Note: Links and references are made to websites which are intended to help the user with further information. The BRC cannot, however, be responsible for the content or continued existence of any external website. It should also be noted that legislation and standards change frequently and a user should confirm for themselves that any references are current and still applicable.